THE DRAMA

ITS LAW AND ITS TECHNIQUE

BY

ELISABETH (WOODBRIDGE,) Ph.D. *Morris*

32698

ALLYN AND BACON

Boston   New York   Chicago

DAT

Norwood Press
J. S. Cushing & Co. — Berwick & Smith
Norwood, Mass., U.S.A.

PREFACE

———◦◦———

FREYTAG'S *Technik des Dramas*, written thirty-five years ago, remains up to this time the best work of its kind. Yet its defects of manner and of arrangement are apparent even to the casual reader, and they become yet more evident when the book is subjected to the test of the college class-room. Such a test — one for which the book was never intended — obscures its merits, which are many, and emphasizes its defects, which might appear few and superficial, but which are peculiarly irritating to both teacher and student. Yet the need of such a book is indicated by the number of treatises on the drama which have appeared since Freytag wrote. All of these that I have seen, however, are either too exclusively philosophical, and in their theorizing about the art ignore the practical details of the craft, or they are not philosophical enough, and in their preoccupation with the craft lose sight of the fundamental principles, the absolute standards, of the art.

In this, as in all other essentials, Freytag was sound; his proportionate emphasis is right, and when I first began to realize the defects of the book, I thought that by making some changes it could be rendered more practically available while no less suggestive. I soon discovered, however, that it was not possible to fit Freytag's discussion into the Procrustean framework of my own plan. His book lacks system, but it does possess the unity that must always characterize the utterances, however careless, of an honest and conscientious thinker. My book, I saw, might rectify some of the faults of the original, but would fall short of its merits. So I laid Freytag quite aside, and wrote the following chapters with as little regard as possible to the discussions in the *Technik*. " As little as possible," — for to make any claim to entire independence would be preposterous. No one can read the utterances of a thoughtful critic and veteran in stage-craft like Freytag without being influenced by them. Even if one has arrived independently at the theories and the judgments therein contained, the formulation and illustration of these theories and judgments by another mind must affect him, if not by altering his thought, at least by enriching its subject-matter. I wish, therefore, to make a comprehensive acknowledgment of my indebtedness to the *Technik*. Comprehensive and general it must be, for just because his book, despite its diffuseness and its desultoriness, is vital and fundamental, it is impossible to lay a finger on the exact places where I am in its debt.

One of the chief merits of Freytag's work is its mass of illustrative comments on ancient and modern dramas. More especially was his use of the Greek dramatists valuable and suggestive, and I hesitated before determining to omit from this treatment any such detailed discussion. Without a sympathetic familiarity with Æschylus, Sophocles, and Euripides for tragedy, and with Aristophanes for comedy, no one can claim the right to "judge righteous judgment" in things dramaturgic. When Freytag wrote, such a familiarity was scarcely to be gained without years of toil ; since his time, modern classical scholarship has experienced a wonderful growth, bearing fruit in a number of critical treatises whose profound learning is informed by philosophic insight and delicate taste, is directed by a sense for historic proportion, is dominated by just æsthetic standards. With such works at hand as the treatises of Jebb, of Butcher, of Haigh, any detailed treatment of the ancient drama would be presumptuous, not to say superfluous, and its place is more fittingly taken by the bibliography at the end of the volume, which points out to the student some of the guides to whom he will commit himself when he shall explore this part of the field.

Of Freytag's illustrations from modern drama, many are based on German plays, and are thus less illuminating to the average American reader — even the college student — than to the German audience for whom they were intended ; hence they greatly increase the bulk of the book without adding proportionately to its effectiveness. I have confined my illustrations more strictly to English literature, using the drama of other nations only where it is needed for comparison. Such a method is theoretically lawful as well as practically expedient, since English drama was in its formative period — that is, up to Dryden — scarcely at all influenced by any other drama save the Roman and, chiefly indirectly, the Greek. With our own contemporary drama it is different. It is not possible to set up a language-barrier when our English and American stages are occupied with the plays of Italian, French, German, and Scandinavian writers.

Of contemporary drama Freytag's book takes almost no account. Indeed, when he wrote, the renaissance, if we may venture to call it so, of drama had only just set in. Ibsen had been writing plays only a few years, and his greatest were yet to come ; Sudermann was six years old ; Hauptmann was an infant; Fulda was not yet born, nor was Maeterlinck, nor Rostand, the brilliant actor-dramatist who is now hailed by some of his countrymen as their young Shakespeare ; in England a few critics were hopelessly hoping that the drama was not really so dead as it seemed. Small wonder that Freytag's mention of modern work had rather the character of an exhortation and a warning than of a critical judgment. But in the last thirty years many good plays, many brilliant ones, some great ones, have been written, and it is well not to ignore them. In the ordinary college courses it is, indeed, scarcely possible to lay much emphasis on these, yet it is unfortunate to treat the drama as though it came to an end, for England in 1616, and for Germany in 1832. Such an attitude lends color of truth to the assertion that the drama is no longer a living art form. One of the signs of its life is that it is changing ; and we must not be deceived by the frequent presentations of Shakespeare's plays into thinking that our stage is like the Elizabethan, or that our Shakespeare is the Shakespeare of Elizabeth and of James. In the study of drama Shakespeare must be our centre, but just as we cannot arrive at the truest judgment if we leave out the Greeks, so too we cannot if we ignore our own contemporaries.

Finally, there is one great section of the drama which Freytag left untouched, — comedy. Yet it is present as an element in every one of Shakespeare's plays, it is the predominant element in many of them, and a discussion of the drama which ignores this is, not *Hamlet* with Hamlet left out, but something more preposterous — *Henry IV* with Falstaff left out.

For an exhaustive, or even a fairly satisfactory, discussion of dramatic comedy an entire volume is needed ; such a volume ought to be written. In the three chapters here devoted to the subject I have tried merely to make a survey of the field, to suggest points of view whence it may be studied, to point out lines along which it may be explored. So little has it been investigated that I cannot offer the student even the nucleus for a bibliography. My hope is that others may come to realize the fascination of this branch of dramatic theory, and that more may be done to illuminate this, at present the most complex and the least adequately treated subject in the realm of literary criticism.

CONTENTS

PART I. — LAW

the relation of the individual to the race and to the highest forces of life, the idea of freedom, and the conception of the divine being, all these have undergone great changes." This is true, yet the more familiar one grows with the Greek drama the more one comes to realize that in the fundamental constitution of human nature there has been little change, and that in proportion as the drama is great it is the same for all ages. Or, if there are in this respect great essential differences, — as there are certainly great superficial ones, — we English are closer to the Greeks in sympathy than we are to some peoples of more recent times, for example, the French of the seventeenth century, and are more at one with the writer of *Œdipus Tyrannus* than with the writer of *Athalie*.

The two elements that are emphasized in dramatic treatment of human nature are, broadly speaking, free will and causality. It is a commonplace of criticism to say that the Greek drama presented the latter, the modern drama the former, and indeed the Greek and the modern use of these two elements is different. But the doctrine of the freedom of the individual is not new, it is as old as the words, "The soul that sinneth, *it* shall die." The doctrine which sees the individual borne remorselessly forward to his fate by forces which he did not initiate is not confined to Greece, it is as old as the first commandment in the Decalogue, or the words, "The fathers have eaten sour grapes, and the children's teeth are set on edge"; but it is also as modern as Ibsen. The ancient world laid greater stress on the second of these two truths, the modern world on the first, but it is only the proportionate emphasis that has changed: nothing old has been wholly lost, nothing really new has been added.

In discussing any art it is possible to treat it in two ways, according as one considers the principles or laws that underly it as an art, or the rules of technique that govern it as a craft. In the first aspect it is brought into more or less close relation with all art; in the second aspect it needs a narrower and more detailed treatment of those things which mark it off from the other arts. The following discussion has attempted to open up the subject first in the more general aspect, and then in the more specific.

Like all art, the drama, to be of value at all, must have truth; to be coherent and effective, it must have unity; to command our veneration, it must have that quality which the Greeks called σπουδή, and which we call greatness, seriousness, nobility. In one sense, any one of these qualities, deeply interpreted, includes the others, but it is possible also to separate them in thought. It has seemed best to take them thus separately and then to try to follow up the two main lines, the tragic and the comic, along which dramatic art has developed.

The Drama

PART I — LAW

CHAPTER I

POETIC TRUTH

ALL art, said Aristotle, is imitation. That he did not mean by this the mere copying or mirroring of facts is sufficiently clear from his remarks about the ideal and philosophic character of poetry: "Tragedy represents men as better than they are," [1] "It should preserve the type and yet ennoble it." [2] In the light of such passages, the word "imitation" takes on another significance from that we might at first be inclined to give it, but it is still misleading, and it seems better to substitute the broader term, "poetic truth." What does this mean, and what does it imply?

All art, and hence all great drama, is in its nature both universal and personal, both general and selective. The painter cannot, for example, paint every leaf of a tree, and if he did so his painting would certainly be more unsatisfactory to us than if he had worked with less minuteness. His art lies in determining which of the impres-

[1] *Poetics*, II.   [2] *Ib.*, XV.

sions into which the infinitely complex total which we call "tree" may be resolved — which of these is to be preserved as essential, which may be rejected. No two artists would ever make quite the same choice, yet each might be, artistically, true to the subject. Each would, if he were a great artist, give us something better than the landscape itself, he would interpret it to us — make it mean more than it had before. Millet once said, in effect, "A flock of sheep must be regarded by the painter, not as a collection of animals, but as one single huge animal, moving on many feet, and it must be so painted." And it is because Millet himself painted sheep in this way that his work is really art. To take another illustration, there is a certain living artist who has wonderful power in drawing the urchins of London's streets, conveying, with a few seemingly careless strokes, the very life and movement of the boys. It is said that he first makes a rather detailed drawing of his subject, then goes over his work, eliminating line after line, until he has reduced it, as it were, to its lowest terms, and there remains no line not absolutely necessary. The finished product, with its appearance of carelessness, is really the result of the most careful selection. It is conceivable that such a process should all have been mental, and nothing have appeared on paper but the final result; conceivable, too, that it might be partly or wholly unconscious on the part of the artist; but the process, or something like it, is characteristic

of all art, and in proportion as the artist is great
will his selective power be true and unerring,
never rejecting the significant and retaining the
unessential. To this end, however, he needs large
and deep knowledge of his subject. Wordsworth
said that a simple recital of the facts of a given
phenomenon might be at once formally accurate
and essentially untrue because it had been made
either mechanically or ignorantly, noting the unessential and the significant without discriminating
between them. Such discrimination comes with
knowledge, which enables us to check our observation of particular instances by a knowledge of the
universal, gained through observation of other
particular instances.

It will now be evident what was meant by saying
that art is in its nature both universal and personal
or selective. It becomes the one by means of the
other, for the selection will reject the accidental
and temporary and retain the essential and permanent. In this selective process the personality of
the artist is tested; upon his personality depends
the value of his work to others. If it is deep
enough and big enough to be in unison with the
individuality (if the expression is legitimate) of
humanity, he will see in his subject, be it landscape or human soul, the things that all humanity
must see when it looks deeply enough, though it
may need his quickened vision to point them out.
Thus the artist must be at once different from his
fellow-man, and like him. "Once in a while an

individual Ideal, when expressed, enlightens the world of art, and then we have the artistic genius; he is the prophet who shows to others an ideal field which they at once recognize as effective for themselves, although but for him it would have been unknown to them. To express his own ideal must be the artist's work."[1] Of the ideal in this sense Amiel's remark is true: "The ideal, after all, is truer than the real; for the ideal is the eternal element in perishable things: it is their type, their sum, their *raison d'être*, their formula in the book of the Creator, and therefore at once the most exact and the most condensed expression of them."[2]

The danger in this selective art-process is evident, especially if we note some phases of it in painting. The extremists of the so-called "impressionist" school are simply carrying this process to its farthest issue. They reproduce of a landscape only a single aspect. All its possibilities of suggestion, its complexity and shading, are swept away to make room for the artist's single impression. The result is rather remarkable. If one happens to approach such a picture from the right direction, with exactly the right light, and in a peculiarly receptive mood, one may receive from it an impression startlingly vivid. If, on the other hand, these conditions are not fulfilled, the picture may be absolutely meaningless to us. The reason is plain enough. The artist has so narrowed his

[1] H. R. Marshall, *Æsthetic Principles*, p. 97.
[2] Amiel, *Journal*, p. 105.

presentation of impressions that it appeals to but few besides himself — it has become personal past the point of contact with others.

The same thing occurs in literature, though it is not so easily demonstrable. Schopenhauer is a case of the too narrowly selective, the viciously personal. He attempts satire, let us say; what results? Often enough, it is not satire, but invective, more or less hysterical. He is giving us things as they appear to him, but they appear to him as they do not appear to a sane man, and his work becomes interesting, not as art, but as pathology. If one would see the difference between satire and anger, that is, between legitimate and illegitimate personality, compare him with Juvenal or Swift at their best, or compare the fourth part of *Gulliver's Travels* with the first three parts.

It is in finding the mean between this personal narrowness that is too selective, and the photographic impersonality that is not selective at all, that the individuality of the artist, his training and his ideals, are tested. It is this that determines how much his work shall possess of what we may call poetic, or artistic, truth. The difference between such truth and the truth of philosophy is not so much in the final result as in the means employed to reach it. The philosopher seeks to discover the essential and universal, and to state it in terms of the universal. The artist seeks to state it in terms of the particular. If he wishes to present the contrast between the misguided human

heart, preoccupied with its gloomy or ghastly
criminal purposes, and the sane and kindly standards of the world of freer men, the philosopher
will state this in terms of universal application;
the poet may symbolize it by the rough and sudden knocking at a castle gate, and the drowsy
murmurs of a sleepy porter.

Such a selective process is forced upon the
dramatist, also, by the practical conditions of his
problem. A play must, when acted, not exceed
three hours, but this is an extreme estimate, and
includes the time for scene-shifting and other
waits ; the business of the play itself ought not to
use more than two-thirds of this time. He has,
then, two hours in which to present his action,
with its causes and results. Obviously, there are
in real life few cases where such an action occu-
pies so short a time; it is more apt to stretch over
months or years, and its links are "the little,
nameless, unremembered acts" of our daily life.
The artist cannot possibly reproduce all these, and
he must, therefore, be in a sense "untrue" to his
model.[1] Yet, if he could reproduce them, he would
not. For life, nature, in itself, as distinguished
from nature as seen by us, is unemphatic. Its so-
called contrasts, its humor, its varying emphasis,
its "meaning," have their existence, not in the
things themselves, but in the mind of the observer.
It is, therefore, the artist's part to supply these, to
mould his material, impressing upon it the stamp

[1] Cf. *infra*, pp. 14–16.

of his mind, and thus giving it emphasis, proportion, perspective, — which brings us back again to the selective process. Out of the infinite series of occurrences he chooses such links as seem to him most important, or such as may be made to symbolize more than themselves. These critical moments he emphasizes, the rest he lets go, trusting that from what we see we will infer what we do not see.[1]

Take *Macbeth*. The dramatist must present to us the moral ruin, — the spiritual disintegration of a man, with its inner causes. What does he do? He selects his moments, presents these, and lets them stand for all that goes between. We first hear of our hero as a high-minded and courageous soldier. Then we see him, fresh from victory, receive the first suggestion of greater honors to be won; we see how the idea takes hold of him, and we suspect that one so easily touched must have been less sound at heart than we and others had supposed. What goes on in his mind immediately after this we are not told, but after the scenes with Lady Macbeth, we can look back and imagine. That is, we find ourselves responding to the poet's demand, we are become co-workers with him. After the murder, again, we get no insight into Macbeth's inner life until after he has been made king. Then comes the banquet-scene, which, brief as it is, throws a blaze of light backward over the

[1] Cf. the discussion of "the unities" in the following chapter, especially pp. 14–19.

interval. We recognize with perfect certitude the disintegration that has been going on in a spirit that we now see to have been never really strong, either for good or evil. And now our mind can go forward without teaching, we shall expect from the harassed king no firmness of touch, we know his spirit is fevered, that he is the slave of his past. For Lady Macbeth we are given no clews through the course of the play until, at the end, we are allowed, for one brief glimpse, to see her off her guard, when her will of steel is relaxed in delirious sleep. But those few lurid moments reveal to us a whole life-history, and it is enough.

If one would realize the tremendous compression of the play, and get the full significance of its method, let him note how another artist has treated a similar theme. Dostoiefsky, in *Crime and Punishment*, gives us the history of a few days in a young man's life, during which he commits a crime, and afterwards, hovering on the verge of madness, undergoes spiritual tortures of the most exquisite kind. His mental processes are given almost from minute to minute, not an hour is unaccounted for. The effect of the whole is, it is true, tremendous; but it is not the kind of effect that art ought to produce, it is not the purified "pity and fear" which makes a subject beautiful in art which is merely terrible in nature. The writer certainly possessed such knowledge of the human soul as is given to few; had he possessed also the power to wield this knowledge, his book would have been one of the grandest art-productions to which a man ever gave being. But one feels that he is not master of his inspiration, he is mastered by it, and the book has upon it the taint of madness from which the author, if we may trust report, was not wholly free. And thus it happens that while Shakespeare had probably a less profound understanding than Dostoiefsky of the inner life of a sin-darkened soul, we feel that his drama is a great artistic creation, whereas of Dostoiefsky's story we feel that it might have been this, but is not.

The discussion has led us to the verge of that never-dying controversy concerning the merits of the realistic and the idealistic in art. To enter upon it would carry us beyond the limits of our subject. Be it suggested, however, that the antithesis between the two terms is not absolute and fixed, for all true art is, as we have seen, ideal, and all true art is based in reality. The difference between the two schools is quantitative, it is a difference in the proportionate emphasis they lay upon these two aspects of art, and their divergence should never be so great as to lead them, the one beyond the limits of art into the photographic, the other beyond the limits of art into the over narrowly personal.

CHAPTER II

DRAMATIC UNITY

FEW sayings have been the occasion of such bitter and long-continued controversy as Aristotle's remarks on the unity of the drama. For this reason, and because they furnish a convenient point of departure, it may be well to quote his own words :

"Tragedy is an imitation of an action, that is complete, and whole, and of a certain magnitude. . . . A whole is that which has beginning, middle, and end. A beginning is that which does not itself follow anything by causal necessity, but after which something naturally is or comes to be. An end, on the contrary, is that which itself naturally follows some other thing, either by necessity, or in the regular course of events, but has nothing following it. A middle is that which follows something as some other thing follows it. A well-constructed plot, therefore, must neither begin nor end at haphazard, but conform to the type here described." [1]

"Unity of plot does not, as some persons think, consist in the unity of the hero. For infinitely various are the incidents in one man's life, which cannot be reduced to unity; and so, too, there are many actions of one man out of which we cannot make one action. . . . As therefore, in the other imitative arts, the imitation is one, when the object imitated is one, so the plot, being an imitation of an action, must imitate

[1] Aristotle, *Poetics*, VII.

one action and that a whole, the structural union of the parts being such that, if any one of them is displaced or removed, the whole will be disjointed and disturbed."[1]

"Epic poetry agrees with Tragedy in so far as it is an imitation in verse of characters of a higher type. . . . They differ, again, in length: for Tragedy endeavors, as far as possible, to confine itself to a single revolution of the sun, or but slightly to exceed this limit; whereas the Epic action has no limits of time."[2]

The first two passages quoted, emphasizing the need for what is technically known as "unity of action," will be seen to have permanent and essential validity. The last passage is evidently a passing generalization made from the usage of Aristotle's contemporaries. It was, however, taken up by the French of the early sixteenth century and, under the title "unity of time," exalted to the position of a chief canon in dramatic art. A third requirement, that of "unity of place," though not even suggested by Aristotle, was taken for granted, partly as a corollary of the unity of time, partly in imitation of Greek and Senecan usage. These three canons, supported by the authority of the French Academy, and, after some resistance, accepted and defended by Corneille, determined the form of French drama until the beginning of this century, when Victor Hugo, in *Hernani*, broke bounds, and the "Romantic" reaction became powerful. In Germany the drama for a time slavishly followed French models, but the break

[1] Aristotle, *Poetics*, VIII. [2] *Ib.*, V.

with the unities came somewhat earlier than in
France, and may be taken as dating from Lessing's
notes on dramatic writing, published between 1767
and 1769. In England the period of great drama
fell so much earlier than in France or in Germany,
that it escaped almost altogether the tyranny of
" classic " tradition. To Shakespeare, Aristotle can
have been little more than a name, and though
Seneca's tragedies were translated in his lifetime,
their influence was only one of the factors which
determined the form of the national drama.[1]

Yet, relatively small as was their influence in
our own literature, the " unities " have been too important elsewhere to be passed over in a discussion
of the drama. Moreover, the very absurdities into
which they led their adherents are instructive as to
the true basis of dramatic theory. Nothing, for example, could be more suggestive than the treatise
in which Corneille[2] defends *The Three Unities, of
Action, of Time, and of Place*. A few extracts will
indicate his position.

"The rule regarding the unity of time is based upon this
remark of Aristotle, 'that the tragedy ought to confine the
duration of its action within one revolution of the sun, or to
try to exceed this but slightly.'[3] These words have given
occasion to this famous controversy, whether they ought to

[1] For the blending of the Senecan and the national tradition,
cf. R. Fischer, *Zur Kunstentwicklung der Englischen Tragödie.*

[2] P. Corneille, Discours III, *Des Trois Unités.*

[3] Note Corneille's mistranslation of Aristotle, which really
begs the whole question. Compare Butcher's translation, quoted
above, p. 11.

be understood to mean a natural day of twenty-four hours, or an artificial day of twelve. . . . For my part, I find that there are subjects which it is so inconvenient to reduce within so brief a time, that not only would I grant them the entire twenty-four hours, but I would even avail myself of the license allowed by the philosopher to exceed this number a little, and would without scruple extend it to thirty."

In support of the rule he argues thus :

"The dramatic poem is an imitation, or, better, a portrait of the actions of men; and there is no doubt that portraits are the more excellent in proportion as they the more closely resemble their original. The representation [of a drama on the stage] lasts two hours, and the verisimilitude would be perfect if the action which it presented did not demand more for its actual occurrence. Let us not, then, fix upon either twelve hours or twenty-four, but let us compress the action of the poem into as brief a space as we possibly can, in order that its representation have the greater verisimilitude and be the more perfect."

As to unity of place, he admits that the rule is not found either in Horace or in Aristotle, but he nevertheless holds it binding, and characterizes as "un peu licencieuse" the interpretation of it which would allow a single drama to represent such places as a man could go to and return from in a day. He goes on :

"I could wish, in order not to offend the spectator in any way, that what we represent before him in two hours could actually take place in two hours, and that what we make him see, on a stage that is immovable, could confine itself to one room, or one hall, according to choice; but often this is so inconvenient, not to say impossible, that it is necessary, for place as for time, to admit some enlargement of the limits."

He concludes that in cases of absolute necessity it is sufficient that the action be confined within the walls of a single city. At the close of his treatise, however, the common sense of the practical playwright overcomes for a moment the conventionality — never quite genuine — of the Academician, and asserts itself in the impatient remark :

" It is easy for the theorists to be rigid; but if they were to give to the public six or a dozen poems of this sort, they would perhaps widen their rules even more than I have done, when they had seen by experience what restraint their precision causes, and how many beautiful things it banishes from our stage."

Evidently the trouble here arises from a misuse of the word " imitation," and a misconception of what " truth to nature " really is. Art does not copy nature, it follows and interprets it, and Corneille's first proposition, about which he says " there is no doubt " — namely, that the more closely the stage presentation copies the actual events the more perfect is the drama — this proposition is false and subversive of good art ; if he had followed it consistently, he would not have been the great artist he was.

On the other hand, the practice of " following these rules at a distance " has something to be said for it. Shakespeare's dramas would have been better if they had not taken quite so much license. The structure of *Lear* is marred by the too frequent changes of scene, not because these destroy the illusion, but because every such change demands a fresh adjustment of the reader's mind to the new conditions, and such use of his energies is waste of his energies unless there is some compensating gain. In *Antony and Cleopatra* we have an illustration of the way in which bad artistic form may almost nullify the effectiveness of the artist's real perceptions; for the noble scenes scattered through the play do not wholly atone for the sprawling, helter-skelter character of the treatment.

In modern plays the elaborateness of the scenery has taken the place of the "classic" tradition as a check on frequent changes of scene, and, except in plays that are chiefly spectacular, the tendency is to cut down scene-shifting, especially within the act. The greater emphasis, too, on the inner rather than the outer aspects of the dramatic situation[1] may have had something to do with the simplification of setting and compactness of treatment that marks the work of at least some groups of modern dramatists. It may be noted in the plays of the young German writers, Sudermann, Hauptmann, Fulda; it is yet more striking in the dramas of Ibsen, some of which preserve the same scene throughout, while two, *Ghosts* and *John Gabriel Borkman*, observe the unity of time in almost Corneille's strictest interpretation. The same is true of Sudermann's *Die Heimath*,[2] and it is interesting to note that these two plays, which have

---

[1] Cf. for an expansion of this, the comparison between Shakespeare and Browning, pp. 129-133.

[2] Acted by Duse and by Bernhardt under the title *Magda*.

roused more than common interest on the stage as well as among the reading public, show such conformity to the standards of a past age. But it is also significant that all three of these plays resemble the Greek drama in presenting to us the culminating point of an action that has been going on for years; the plays themselves include little more than would be found in the last act of a Shakespearean drama, and their likeness to the classic form may be taken as a natural result of this essential similarity of theme.

The gain in these cases, however, is not due, as Corneille would have said, to the greater accuracy with which the facts can be copied, but to the greater economy of attention made possible by concentration in the treatment and by elimination of distracting features. Ibsen's *Ghosts*, which presents the occurrences of a single day in Mrs. Alving's drawing-room, is not, because of this, a whit more "true" than Shakespeare's *Macbeth*, whose action covers at least months and ranges between England and Scotland. Except when they are of importance for other reasons than those Corneille gives, the unities of time and of place may be set aside as non-essential. The dramatist cannot copy his subject, — he ought not to do so, — and the extent to which he copies its outer setting cannot be rigidly prescribed to him. Since he must often make us feel, by means of a few phrases, a soul's long-drawn agonies, why may he not also make us feel, by means of a two hours' play, a soul's life-history? Surely, if he can, he may.

But if these requirements concerning time and place were conventional rules imposed upon drama from without, that concerning action is a vitally grounded law, growing out of the very nature of the art-form; and it is characteristic of the directness and truth of Aristotle's thought that he is not content with a casual mention of this point, as in the matter of the time-limit, but pauses to emphasize and elaborate his idea, — reverts to it now and again to add some further comment from another point of view.

What he means by unity of action he makes very clear. It is organic unity, he explains, not formal or verbal, that he wants, and this is not necessarily attained by making the actions all centre about one man. He hits the point exactly when he says that it is the action *chosen*, which must be a whole. It must, that is, be such an action as can be adequately set forth, with its "beginning, middle, and end," during the two hours allotted to the poet, and by the means at his command. This effectually cuts him off from treating certain themes. National issues, for instance, cannot be handled by him, except as they touch upon individual human lives. They may, indeed, have a certain large unity, they are as truly controlled by laws, and as open to philosophic treatment as is the life of a single man, but the drama cannot handle them. Gibbon's *Decline and Fall of the Roman*

c

Empire may, by a figure of speech, be called a magnificent drama. It has, on a gigantic scale, complete and organic unity; it has, in the true sense, a beginning, a middle, and an end. It does for the Roman Empire what Shakespeare does for *Macbeth* — portrays a process of disintegration and ruin, and traces it to its source in contravention of the laws of human life and intercourse. But Gibbon's subject-matter is outside the dramatist's realm. He may touch upon it, as Shakespeare does in *Julius Cæsar*, but the centre of interest will be not the state, but the man, as here it is Brutus. Where this is not the case, as in several of Shakespeare's historical plays, *Henry VIII*, or *Henry V*, or *King John*, the play is in so far imperfect. That even Shakespeare erred thus often is not surprising. Such plays appealed to the patriotism of his audience and ministered to their inherent Teutonic love of incident and spectacle; they were to those times what the plays based on Napoleon's life have within recent years been to ours. But such productions are not good dramatic art. The play must have, not merely a running story that can be told, but a centre, and a determined line of development. Shelley expressed this when he wrote, in his preface to *The Cenci*, "Such a story, if told so as to present to the reader all the feelings of those who once acted it, their hopes and fears, their confidences and misgivings, their various interests, passions, and opinions, acting upon and with each other, yet all conspiring to one tremendous end, would be as light to make apparent some of the most dark and secret caverns of the human heart." It is this "conspiring to one tremendous end" that is the test of the plot and of the characters.

But it is a test that cannot be applied by rule of thumb. Aristotle, indeed, speaks, in his cool, definite way, of "the structural union of the parts being such that if any one of them is displaced or removed, the whole will be disjointed and disturbed."[1] Such a test can well be applied to the dramas of Sophocles: — try to "cut" the *Antigone* or the *Œdipus*, either by reducing the number of characters or by removing incidents ; it is like hewing away a limb from a living creature. But, with modern plays, it is another matter. It is true the French of the sixteenth century, following a perverted classic tradition, attempted to attain this same kind of unity: their plays have few underplots, the number of characters is kept as low as possible. But to the Teutonic mind, these productions lack the power that comes of unified complexity, while they have not, on the other hand, the lyric intensity and vitality of the Greek drama. Schopenhauer puts this feeling perhaps over-vigorously, as is his way, but effectively, when he says that the French tragedies "in general observe this [unity] so strictly that the course of the drama is like a geometrical line without breadth. There it is always a case of 'Only get on! *Pensez à votre affaire !*'"

[1] *Poetics*, VIII.

In the modern French drama, however, as in all English, we have to face the question of episode and subordinate characters — problems which virtually did not exist for Aristotle, since the severely narrow limits of tragedy did not admit of any episode in our sense of the word, and minor characters scarcely appeared. Shakespeare's dramas, on the contrary, abound in episodes that have little apparent connection with the main plot, many of which could be cut out without "disjointing" or "disturbing" the structure of the play. In actual stage presentation some of these actually are left out, and, unless we sit book in hand, we are not likely to notice the omissions. This is less true of the tragedies, however, and in the greatest of these we shall usually find that many of these seemingly trifling incidents are set there with a purpose, and make toward the main end. "Almost too copiously and with apparent carelessness, the great artist fastens his golden ornaments in all parts of his piece; but he who goes to unclasp them finds them grown iron-fast into the texture of the whole." [1]

That a given scene may be omitted without leaving the story of the action incomplete is, of course, no indication that such a scene is superfluous, or runs counter to true unity. Many scenes are needed to give shading to character, to supply contrast, or background. Here, again, nothing can be decided by rule, and even about the greatest of the plays we find that opinion differs. The

[1] Freytag, *Technik des Dramas*, p. 45.

underplot in *Lear* is, according to one critic, a blemish, since it is "connected but loosely with the main action," and "retards the movement and needlessly renders the whole more bitter." Others[1] regard this same underplot as a source of strength, since it furnishes a reflection of the main action and thus heightens the total effect, as the subordinate theme in a symphony may be a reflection or variant of the principal theme, or as the subordinate lines of a picture may follow the lead of the main color masses. It matters less which judgment we finally adopt than the manner in which we arrive at the judgment. The only tribunal of appeal is taste, but it should be taste that has been trained by long and thoughtful familiarity with the best art.

[1] Vide Ulrici: *Shakespeare's Dramatic Art*, I, 437 ff.; Brandes: *William Shakespeare*, II, 135.

CHAPTER III

"TRAGEDY," said Aristotle, "is an imitation of an action that is serious." The word he uses here, σπουδαίας, is explained by Butcher as uniting the two notions of grave and great; it has been paraphrased by Arnold in the expression "high and excellent seriousness," and these phrases come as near as any to indicating a certain quality of greatness which we all recognize as indispensable to the serious drama.

To begin with, one must carefully guard oneself against the mistake of confusing greatness of subject with greatness of treatment. Only the second can produce greatness in the art-product, yet these two things have been, and still are, constantly confounded. Donne's poems, we are told, are sublime because their theme is so. Milton's *Paradise Lost* is greater than Virgil's *Æneid* by the whole difference in grandeur between the conceptions of the two poems, one dealing with the founding of Rome, the other with the fall of man from his first state. It is easy to see the absurdity of such judgments, taking them individually, and nearly as easy to fall into similar absurdities on one's own account.

The reason may be that there is in such notions a root of truth. For, if the subject does not make the poem, at least subject and poem have a common source, the one being chosen, the other created, by the poet; and it is quite probable that if a "sublime" subject genuinely appeals to a poet, he has in him elements of sublimity, although these may not be accompanied by the power to create a sublime poem.

And we must make another distinction, between the subject-matter as it exists apart from the artist in the actual world of experience, and the subject as recognized by the artist, recreated in his mind as his theme. Sometimes one of these is truly great when the other is not. Thus, a jealous man does not usually impress us as having any elements of greatness, yet Othello is great, because greatly conceived; querulous and impotent old age seems unpropitious for drama, as do the half-crazed murmurs of an old clown, yet Lear and his fool are among the greatest dramatic creations. Such greatness is due, not to the original subject-matter, but to the poet who, whatever his theme, views it so truly and deeply that he reaches its inner significance as human life — and it is in the depths of human life that greatness will be found, if found anywhere.

The necessity that tragedy and the serious drama shall possess an element of greatness or largeness — call it nobility, elevation, what you will — has always been recognized. The divergence has come when men have begun to say what they mean by this quality, and — which is much the same thing — how it is to be attained. Even Aristotle, when he begins to analyze methods, sounds, at first hearing, a little superficial. The hero must be, he says, "one who is highly renowned and prosperous, — a personage like Œdipus, Thyestes, and other illustrious men of such families."[1] Now we are used to seeing tragic effects produced in the treatment of characters who are neither renowned nor of noble family. Yet, for his own time, Aristotle was right. For dramatic action means struggle, and struggle of the most intense kind; the dramatic agent must therefore possess, not only latent passion and potential energy, but opportunity which shall make this energy kinetic. Such opportunity came in the past chiefly to such men as by birth or fortune were placed in positions of power, who were forced to take part in affairs having large issues and demanding positive and individual activity. They had, as others did not have, opportunity for self-expression in action; they had greatness thrust upon them, while the average man of their times was lost in the corporate body. For, even in Greece, society had not yet wholly freed itself from the tradition of tribal solidarity and tribal responsibility, and the individual appears in half-relief, epic rather than dramatic, controlled by events rather than originating action. This the Greek dramatists felt, and it was one of the

[1] *Poetics,* XIII.

reasons why they sought their heroes in the rolls of kings and their actions in the annals of nations. They were right, and Aristotle merely stated, in his somewhat bare way, a generalization from their practice. What is wrong is the assumption made by later theorists and dramatic artists that, because the Greeks had found their tragic heroes among kings, therefore royalty was sufficient to constitute a tragic hero, and a great national issue was, as such, fit subject for a tragic action. Thus Racine, in *Athalie*, has chosen a crisis in Hebrew history. He has not, however, presented to us actions in themselves of great tragic import — or rather, he has not interpreted to us the tragic import of the actions which he presents. A vicious queen, who has won her throne by murder, retains it by force. By a successful *coup d'état* of the minority, she is deposed and put to death. This theme has historical importance; it lacks dramatic importance because the sources of the action are not rooted in the spiritual nature of the heroine or of any other of the actors. Yet two points in the action might have furnished a theme that would have been truly dramatic. One is the conflict between the queen's ambitious lust of power and her impulse of love for the boy who proves her rival. Another is the conflict of impulses in the old general, Abner, whose instinctive patriotism bids him free his country from an oppressive and unrighteous rule, but whose military training enjoins him to render unquestioning obedience to his sovereign.   Each of these themes is suggested in Racine's drama, and as each suggestion occurs the reader awaits its further development, but awaits it in vain.   The author evidently had in mind the historical importance of his action rather than its spiritual import.

Compare the way in which Shakespeare has treated a similar subject. *Julius Cæsar*, like *Athalie*, is concerned with a crisis in a nation's history, where a tyrant is overcome by a small but steadfast minority.   But the tragic interest does not depend upon our knowledge that the fate of Rome hung upon the result of Brutus' conspiracy. This fact, kept in the background, or used as a motive force in the half-prophetic consciousness of Brutus himself, does indeed enhance the appeal to our interest, but the nearer and stronger appeal is made through the individuality of the men Cæsar, Antony, Brutus, Cassius, while the tragic theme is found in the spiritual experiences of Brutus, torn by a double and conflicting allegiance.   Thus, in Brutus, Shakespeare has done exactly the thing that Racine missed doing, and *Julius Cæsar* has in this respect a greatness that *Athalie* wholly lacks.

That the spiritual issue might have been made yet clearer may be acknowledged; it will certainly be recognized if we extend our field of comparison, and consider Browning's use of a similar theme in *Strafford*.   As in *Athalie*, as in *Julius Cæsar*, there is in *Strafford* the tyrant, the oppressed people crying for relief, the reluctant, sad-hearted

leaders shrinking from the issue, yet forced to meet
it. But here, as in *Julius Cæsar*, the greatness of the
interests involved does not constitute the tragedy,
though it furnishes the occasion for it and makes
for it a background of sombre grandeur. The
tragic interest gathers about the three figures Pym,
Charles, Strafford; it centres in the spiritual experiences of the great statesman who is forced by
fate to do violence to one-half of himself in being
true to the mandates of the other half. All the
powers of the dramatist are exerted toward this one
end — toward laying bare the inner life of the man,
the mortal pain of a great soul forced to be untrue
to itself. To say that *Strafford* is a greater drama
than *Julius Cæsar* would be at least venturesome; it
would probably be a mistake, for there are many
considerations to be taken into account in the final
judgment of a drama. The three plays are here
presented as a group to illustrate the way in which
political eminence in the actor and national issues
involved in the action may be used or abused by
the dramatist.[1]

It is apparent that a proper use of these elements, as subsidiary aids to dramatic effect, is
entirely legitimate. It is equally apparent that

---

[1] The three, or more particularly the last two, would well repay
study from other points of view. The characters and motiving
of Cæsar as compared with Charles, and of Brutus as compared
with Strafford and Pym, the use made of historical background,
the treatment of the subordinate characters, all these are subjects
that could be so treated as to illuminate the questions of dramatic effect in general.

they must be recognized as subsidiary only, that
they must not be given first place as factors of
this "greatness" which we have been discussing.
The essential requirement is that the dramatic hero
be free to express himself in action, that he be
given scope first to develop and then to express
his individuality ; and material power, social and
political eminence are valuable only because they
furnish these things, and only when they do so.
What is required for great drama is not great political or religious or social issues as such, but the
enlargement of soul and stress of passion that sometimes accompanies great issues. What is needed
for the tragic hero is not the crowned head, but
the royal nature. "Royal" by a figure only, for
such a nature is not now necessarily found among
monarchs; and kings, once singularly fit subjects
for dramatic treatment, are becoming singularly
unfit. The monarch, bound and shackled by con-
stitutional provisions, loses his personality, though
in his private capacity he may still keep his freedom. The very eminence that once gave scope
to his individuality now tends to repress it, and,
private individuality and official greatness being
thus dissevered, the special dramatic meaning of
this greatness is gone; there is no longer the iden-
tity expressed in the significant title, "Œdipus
King."

On the other hand, this freedom and scope for
individuality, no longer the concomitant of royalty as such, is in modern times often found in

the status of the so-called "private" man. The "royal" nature that is developed by power and opportunity, and which in turn uses power and opportunity for its self-expression, may be found in a man whose eminence is social or political; it is even conceivable that a great tragic hero may be found in one who has no apparent "eminence" of any kind. Such a one, it may be said, is Beatrice Cenci, but the case is not clear enough to prove the point. Certainly our modern stage-drama, with its love of "middle-class" subjects, has not yet produced anything really great. On the other hand, it is significant that the greatest classic dramas — those of Shakespeare and of Sophocles, those of Schiller, Euripides, Corneille — all conform to this seemingly superficial rule of Aristotle, as do the greatest English dramas of this century, those of Shelley, of Tennyson, of Browning, and of Swinburne. The German "familien-drama" and the French society drama lack this element of greatness, or where they possess it they too will be found to be in conformity.

There is another consideration which might have motived Aristotle's remark, though it probably did not do so. Dramatic action is not merely action as seen in the outer event, but action viewed in relation to its source in passionate emotion and in relation to its reactionary emotional effect. It is therefore necessary that we understand the spiritual states of the agent, and this is in the main brought about only through his own words. For the medium of the drama is self-expression by the actors, not description by the writer, and self-expression principally in words. But such power of self-expression implies in the agent a large degree of culture of a certain kind, as well as a certain bent of character; in general, men must reach rather a high level, intellectually, before they become sufficiently conscious of their own spiritual states to express them.

In the modern drama, owing to the increased complexity and subtlety of the dramatic motiving, it is increasingly important that we understand the thought as well as the acts of the persons involved. Consider what the play of *Hamlet* would be if its hero were not endowed with the most marvellous power of self-expression, counterbalancing his power of self-repression. Our appreciation of the play depends upon our understanding of the relation between his apparently meaningless acts and his spiritual states, which are deeply significant; and it is because, whether intentionally or not on the author's part, Hamlet does not, after all, adequately express these spiritual states [1] that the drama still remains not perfectly clear in its motiving.

A very recent attempt to introduce the unedu-

[1] Possibly the reason why he does not is because these spiritual states were not clearly conceived by the author himself. He seems to have been working away from an earlier, traditional Hamlet, toward a new conception of the character, but never to have quite freed himself from the earlier tradition. Cf. Corbin: *The Elizabethan Hamlet.*

cated classes into the drama as its central figures
seems only to bear out the principle just developed.
Hauptmann, in *Die Weber*, presents a society of
working people degraded by crushing labor and
hopeless poverty almost to the level of brutes.
The result is not satisfying. There are scenes of
keen pathos, there are scenes with tragic lights,
but the participants have not sufficient power of
self-expression: they need a spokesman. We know
they are hungry, sick, dying, and we pity them;
but they are incoherent, and their incoherence is
none the less baffling because we know that in re-
producing it the author is giving us a faithful portrait of actual conditions. The same material
might have been used with great effect in another
literary form — in the story, for instance, or the
novel, for this form would have given the author a
chance to interpret his characters to the reader, to
speak for them where they cannot speak for themselves. But they are not suitable for dramatic treatment — at least it yet remains to prove them so.

Summing up, then: Aristotle's generalization
from Greek usage is seen to have been borne out
by later dramatic writers, but the reasons for its
validity must be recognized, or there is danger of a
superficial and conventional interpretation. The
use of great national issues is right so long as the
dramatist does not rely for his great effects upon
our knowledge of the great issues involved. It is
well that the hero be outwardly great as well as
inwardly, — the two things will usually go together,

— but the dramatist must not be content to substitute the outward for the inward greatness.

But if this quality of "greatness" does not essentially consist in these things, in what does it essentially consist?

Shelley, in another connection, says:

"The highest moral purpose aimed at in the highest species of the drama is the teaching the human heart, through its sympathies and antipathies, the knowledge of itself." [1] And an answer to the question just propounded would be, that a drama, which deals truly and — which is the same thing — vitally with the human heart in its struggles with itself and with the outer world, will possess greatness and seriousness. Such an answer may seem utterly hackneyed, but it is, in the end, the only one that can be given. For the artist has to do with phenomena, and in the world of phenomena the human spirit — whatever we may think of it absolutely — is relatively the greatest thing we know. There are ideas metaphysical which bring with them a kind of enlargement of mind technically known in Æsthetic as the feeling of sublimity: such are the conceptions of God as found in the Hebrew religion and in some of the religions of the far East, the conception of the soul, or of a future life. Such ideas as these are found in the writings of Dante and of Milton, and it is occasionally suggested that their writings are for this reason greater than, for example,

---

[1] Preface to the *Cenci*.

Shakespeare's. In reply, we may say that it is at least doubtful whether it is the metaphysics of Milton that give him his greatness, while we may be sure it is not this which gives Dante his. But, even if it were so, Shakespeare's defence is clear. With metaphysical notions as such the dramatist has nothing to do. His concern is, first and last, with the human spirit, and these ideas concern him, not directly, but only in so far as they appeal to and influence the men and women whom he is portraying. It is not his province to

> "Assert eternal providence
> And justify the ways of God to men,"

but rather to show the ways of men toward God,— or whatever stands to them for God, — and toward each other. Dante may say:

> "Varamente quant' io del regno santo
> Nella mia mente potei far tesoro,
> Sara ora materia del mio canto." [1]

The dramatist approaches such subjects only in-directly, through his created persons. It is thus that Hamlet gazes out into

> "That undiscovered country from whose bourn
> No traveller returns."

It is thus that Antigone faces death, firm, but hopeless, in those last words of hers:

"Ah, fount of Dirce, and thou, holy sons of Thebe whose chariots are many; ye, at least, will

[1] *Paradiso*, XXXIII.

D

bear me witness, in what sort, unwept of friends,
and by what laws I pass to the rock-closed prison
of my strange tomb, ah me unhappy! who have
no home on the earth or in the shades, no home
with the living or with the dead. . . . Unwept,
unfriended, without marriage-song, I am led forth
in my sorrow on this journey that can be delayed
no more. No longer, hapless one, may I behold
yon day-star's sacred eye; but for my fate no tear
is shed, no friend makes moan." [1]

It is thus that Beatrice looks over the brink,
shuddering:

"My God! can it be possible I have
 To die so suddenly? So young to go
 Under the obscure, cold, rotting, wormy ground!
 To see no more sweet sunshine; hear no more
 Blithe voice of living being; . . .

. . . .

"What! O, where am I? Let me not go mad!
 Sweet heaven forgive weak thoughts! If there should be
 No God, no Heaven, no Earth in the void world;
 The wide, gray, lampless, deep, unpeopled world!
 If all things then should be — my father's spirit, . . .

. . . .

                  . . . "Who ever yet returned
 To teach the laws of death's untrodden realm?
 Unjust, perhaps, as those which drive us now,
 O, whither, whither?" [2]

This is the sublimity of the dramatist. [3] But such
passages as these show also, better than any expo-

---

[1] *Antigone*, trans. Jebb, pp. 161 ff.
[2] Shelley: *The Cenci*, V, 4.
[3] Cf. *infra*, pp. 40–42.

sition can do, the source of the dramatic $\sigma\pi\upsilon\delta\dot{\eta}$ in the poet's interpretative portrayal of human souls. We might say that any human soul, so long as it be strong and positive, — that is, truly alive, — might, if deeply viewed, be a "great" subject. He might not possess the kind of qualities that become dramatic; his story might not have the kind of unity necessary in a play; but simply in this one quality of greatness and seriousness he would be fit. The quality is not, of course, confined to drama; hardly, even, to so-called "serious" writing. It is possessed by Dante and Shakespeare and Sophocles, it is true, but it also underlies Rabelais and pervades Cervantes. It marks every line of Browning's writing, while — to take examples somewhat at random — Tennyson seldom shows it, Byron almost never. But while other forms of writing may possess this quality, the serious drama must possess it. There are other sources of greatness and seriousness: a poem may have it by virtue of its sweep and velocity of thought, as in Byron's *Cain;* or of its nobility of thought and its majestic sound and rhythm, as in Milton; or by a certain large simplicity, as in Keats' *Hyperion.* The serious drama may have all these; it must have the greatness that springs from a wise and vital treatment of human nature.

CHAPTER IV

THE NATURE AND SOURCES OF TRAGIC EFFECT

THE word "tragic," as commonly used, denotes anything sad, especially something having the qualities of suddenness and finality. It is scarcely distinguished from the pathetic, and, though when the two words are brought together a difference is felt, it is a difference rather of intensity than of quality. But for our purposes the word must be interpreted more narrowly, to mean the kind of effect produced by the sight of a losing struggle carried on between a strong but imperfect individuality and the overpowering forces of life. This will do as a rough beginning, as a trial definition, to be corroborated or modified as it is applied to those tragedies which are by universal consent held to be among the greatest. Choosing almost at random, let us take for this purpose the tragedy *Macbeth*, the tragedy *Othello*, and the tragedies whose centre of interest is the figure of Orestes.

In *Macbeth* we have a double protagonist, for a treatment of Lady Macbeth as subordinate involves one in great difficulties. We have here a man in whom are mingled great strength and great weakness: he is a brave and able soldier, but is incapable of prolonged and consistent effort; his thinking is superficial and his morality is therefore not vital and durable; a man of generous and kindly impulses, but open to influence either for good or evil if another stronger and steadier force be brought to bear upon him. Such a force is found in Lady Macbeth. Her mind is cool and steady, and her effectiveness in carrying out any policy she may take up, whether that policy be good or bad, is therefore greater than his could ever be. The occurrence of favorable opportunity, and her ambition for her husband determine her toward evil. Macbeth, morally unsound but wavering in his policy, is upheld by his wife, and together they enter upon the series of acts which end in the ruin of both. The tragic effects are found in their struggles to do that which is impossible — to escape the consequences of their own acts.

Othello presents, stated briefly, a struggle between two natures: the one impulsive, passionate, generous, endowed with tremendous power to love and hate, but not well poised, without controlling judgment; the other cold, intellectually agile, self-sufficient and self-controlled, able to use himself and others as tools with a skill founded in an accurate though limited understanding of human motives. In this struggle, Othello's weakness brings about his fall, but Iago's success is not complete because his understanding is thus limited

— because the world is not, after all, wholly moved
by the motives which he understands and counts
upon. Each falls a victim to the laws of society
which are based in human nature.

In Orestes we have the spectacle of a man who,
through no fault of his own, is placed in a position where he must choose between two evils, and,
whichever he chooses, he will be contravening
some of the most sacred laws of religion and of
nature. He chooses, and bears the retribution
which his act, though necessary, necessarily
involved.

In these instances we find certain constant elements which had been already implied in our trial
definition. There is always a struggle, there is
the fighter, and there is the opposing force. Let
us examine these elements.

And first, the fighter. Our definition said, a
strong but imperfect individuality. It has already
(chap. III) been suggested that the dramatic person must be vital and positive. Not that he must
necessarily act positively; the colorlessness of
much of Hamlet's outer activity is quite different
from that of his two friends, Rosenkranz and Guil-
denstern. It is not the result of forcelessness, but
the resultant of conflicting forces within him.
The hero must be imperfect, because, for one
reason, a perfectly poised character is usually too
nearly invulnerable for the opposing force to get
a firm hold. Aristotle clearly saw this when he
said that the hero must not be a perfectly good

man, but, as we shall see, this provision has to be accepted with some reservations.[1] The deepest reason for it is found in the nature of the opposing force.

For the best form of tragedy is found, according to Hegel, when the opposing force is closely united with the soul of the fighter himself — when it has effected a lodgment in the enemy's trenches and fights from within as well as from without. Such is the case in *Macbeth*, such is Orestes' case, such is the case in *Othello*, such is preëminently the case in *Hamlet* and in *Wallenstein*. The hero is, as it were, his own worst enemy. So that one is almost inclined to state categorically that the hero must be thus imperfect, because the tragic struggle must be within him in order to be truly tragic.

But tempting as it is to generalize from these supreme examples, we must be careful not to construct such a theory of the tragic as will exclude such plays as *Antigone*, and *Romeo and Juliet*. Here we have another class of effects which we cannot ignore, and in which the tragic element is certainly of a different kind from that found in the other group. We have, in each of these cases, a tragic hero or heroes whose struggle is with outer circumstances, and whose fall is necessitated, not by inner weakness, but by the brute strength of external fact. Thus, Antigone is, so far as her tragic end is concerned, a perfect character. But

[1] Cf. *infra*, pp. 117 ff.

a combination of circumstances suddenly arises, because of which she is forced to choose between conformity to a social or political law and obedience to a spiritual or religious law. Her brother's corpse lies unburied outside her native city. Her king and uncle — having over her since her father's death also a father's authority — imperatively commands that the body shall not be buried. This command Antigone feels bound, by all the sacredness of family ties and religious custom, to contravene. She chooses to break the law of the state, and by the state she dies. The story of Orestes might, of course, be similarly interpreted, and thus brought within this group of tragedies.

It may indeed be said that such a death in such a cause is not defeat but triumph, and so it is, from one standpoint. But such a standpoint is not one from which we can judge drama with any practical helpfulness. It would involve us in endless subtleties, probably ending in the assertion that the only thing truly tragic is the moral ruin of a soul,— which would cut out nearly everything in drama except *Macbeth* and Browning's *A Soul's Tragedy*, or at least would swing around the whole emphasis in the tragedies we know, transferring the interest from the so-called "heroes" to the so-called "villains," who, having power only to "kill the body" of their victims, kill, in so doing, their own souls.

Evidently this will not do, and we must return to a simpler and perhaps a somewhat more external way of judging. Antigone may be spiritually a conqueror, — her death is surely amply avenged, — but considered simply as a woman, as a human being with but one earthly life to live, she is conquered. This, indeed, she herself recognizes when she answers the chorus, who have been trying to show her the heroic aspect of her fate:

> " *Chorus.* But 'tis great renown for a woman who hath perished that she should have shared the doom of the godlike, in her life, and afterward in death.
>
> *Antigone.* Ah, I am mocked! In the name of our fathers' gods, can ye not wait till I am gone, — must ye taunt me to my face, O my city, and ye, her wealthy sons? Ah, fount of Dirce, and thou holy ground of Thebe whose chariots are many; ye, at least, will bear me witness, in what sort, unwept of friends, and by what laws I pass to the rock-closed prison of my strange tomb, ah me unhappy! who have no home on the earth or in the shades, no home with the living or with the dead. . . . From what manner of parents did I take my miserable being! And to them I go thus, accursed, unwed, to share their home. Alas, my brother, ill-starred in thy marriage, in thy death thou hast undone my life!" [1]

To change the instance : — the end of the prison-scene in *Faust* means that the girl has won for herself the great spiritual victory:

> " *Marguerite.* Gericht Gottes! Dir hab' ich mich über-geben!
> Dein bin ich, Vater! Rette mich!
> Ihr Engel! Ihr heiligen Schaaren,
> Lagert euch umher, mich zu bewahren!

[1] *Antigone*, trans. Jebb, pp. 155 ff.

> Heinrich !   Mir graut's vor dir.
> *Mephistopheles.*   Sie ist gerichtet!
> *Stimme.*   [von oben]   Ist gerettet! "

But her drama is none the less a tragedy, and
while the "voice from above" proclaims her
"saved," Mephistopheles is, humanly speaking,
entirely right in deeming her "lost." The two
judgments here thus opposed may be taken as
representative of the two standards — the standard
which judges a human life by itself, and sees in
death an ultimate fact; and the standard which
looks beyond and above to a different set of spiritual values, in which death is a comparatively un-
important element, or important only as it acts
upon the hero's nature as a motive. The second
standard may or may not be the true one; the
first seems the only practicable one to apply to art.
For, as we have already said, the artist works with
phenomena only; life has for him only what it
seems to have for those who live it, and death for
him is ultimate because it ends our known activity.[1]

Remembering, then, that there is another way
of judging, we may once more return to our definition of tragedy: as a losing struggle wherein the
opposing and victorious forces may lie either
chiefly within the hero's own nature, in which case
we have a conflict which is chiefly spiritual —
Hamlet, Orestes; or they may lie chiefly outside,
in which case we have a struggle more or less external, the hero remaining unmoved — Antigone,

[1] Cf. *supra*, pp. 32–34, and *infra*, pp. 88–90.

Romeo, and Juliet; or it may be both internal and external — Othello, possibly Wallenstein. Of course in one sense it must always be both, for the spiritual forces of the inner struggle will always have some outward and material embodiment, the outer conflict will always have an answering inner phase.[1] Here, as always, it is a question of proportion, of relative emphasis, and there is no possibility of strict demarcations of classes.

One other element there is which these all have in common, besides the necessity of there being a struggle and a losing one: the element, namely, of causality. Aristotle saw this clearly and laid great emphasis upon it:

"Tragedy is an imitation . . . of events terrible and pitiful. Such an effect is best produced when the events come on us by surprise; and the effect is heightened when, at the same time, they follow from one another. The tragic wonder will then be greater than if they happened of themselves or by accident; for even accidents are most striking when they have an air of design."[2]

"These last [reversal of fortune and recognition] should arise from the internal structure of the plot, so that what follows should be the necessary or probable result of the preceding action. It makes all the difference whether one event is the consequence of another, or merely subsequent to it."[3]

"It is therefore evident that the unravelling of the plot, no less than the complication, must arise out of the plot itself, it must not be brought about by the *Deus ex Machina.* Within the action there must be nothing irrational."[4]

[1] Cf. *infra*, pp. 129 ff.   [2] *Poetics*, IX.   [3] *Ib.*, X.   [4] *Ib.*, XV.

That is to say, the opposing force must derive its power, not only really but evidently, from what has gone before. Aristotle even goes so far as to say that if the event be not really probable, it should at least, by a kind of sleight of hand, be made to seem so.[1] But, if such jugglery is necessary, it means weakness. The drama should be the place where we may see, more easily recognizable than in actual life, the universal operation and validity of irresistible law. *Othello* is not a great tragedy because a husband mistakenly kills his wife, but because he is seen to be, in so doing, the victim and the agent of absolute and remorseless law. *Wallenstein* is not a great tragedy because the general is assassinated, or even because he is a traitor, but because these things are seen to be the inevitable conclusion of the given series of events. The thing which we must be made to feel is, in Amiel's phrase, "The fatality of the consequences which follow upon every human act, — the leading idea of dramatic art and the most tragic element of life."[2]

To take an opposite instance, the following is a true story of our Civil War: A young Confederate soldier had, after months of service, obtained leave to go home for a few weeks. His companions crowded around him, giving him messages to friends, and letters to be sent when he reached a safe district. As he was ready to start he turned back, with the words, "Guess I'll have one more

[1] *Poetics*, XXIV. [2] *Journal*, 6th April, 1851.

look at the Yanks," and went out again to the in-
trenchments. He leaned forward on the ridge,
raised his head above it, and a bullet from the
Union ranks struck him. He fell forward, dead.

Such an event appeals to us with more than
common force, by virtue of its grim irony. It is
one of those accidents which Aristotle would have
said have an air of design, but it is not available
for tragedy — at least, not for the chief event of
tragedy — because it is, after all, accident. It
may, indeed, be said that nothing is accidental,
everything is the result of unvarying law, and this
is certainly true. But not all events bear upon
them the recognizable stamp of this causality, and
there are therefore in our experience a vast number of occurrences which go by the name of accidents. The dramatist may be able by his insight
and power of presentation to take some of these
occurrences out of this category. If he can, they
are his to use. If he cannot, they are not fit material for tragedy; their appearance in drama is a
sign of decay, it is one of the distinguishing characteristics of the "melodramatic." If examples
of this kind of abuse are wanted, they may be
found in almost any of the plays of Beaumont and
Fletcher.

Such an incident as that just given, if not strictly
speaking tragic, is certainly pathetic, and we are
now ready to return to the distinction, suggested at
the beginning of the chapter, between these two
classes of effects. That is pathetic which involves

suffering, unmerited, or out of proportion to guilt, or at least considered without reference to the guilt of the sufferer. It implies a certain passivity on his part, or a resistance so manifestly inadequate as to amount to the same thing. Thus, the sufferings of animals under abuse are pathetic, the sufferings of sick people are so, so is much spiritual suffering which is recognized as inevitable and endured as such. Thus, Ophelia and Desdemona may be called pathetic, while Hamlet and Othello are tragic, and we might multiply examples indefinitely. This is perhaps the reason why children have never been used as tragic heroes. To themselves, their world is great and their emotions intense, and, suffering being a wholly subjective matter, their actual sufferings are doubtless often as great as those of adults. But the dramatist is concerned with act as well as feeling, with struggle as well as pain, and the child has not the command of himself and of the world to meet these requirements. Occasionally the treatment of children in literature, by some singular combination of good fortune and skill and sympathy, does approximate the tragic; it does this in Kipling's remarkable story, *The Drums of the Fore and Aft*. But the means by which the author has attained this result, so far as they are discoverable, only go to prove the truth of the general rule. An interesting instance of its validity may be found in the three Theban plays of Sophocles. In the *Œdipus Rex* Antigone and Ismene are simply pathetic figures, used to enhance the effect of their father's fall. In the *Œdipus Coloneus* Antigone is rising out of this passivity, but she is still in the main pathetic in this sense. In the *Antigone* she has become truly tragic, though retaining a certain pathetic tone, by virtue of the quietness of her resistance.[1]

It is, then, not enough that an incident be pathetic — that the recital of it saddens us. It must not be merely

> "a tale of things
> Done long ago, and ill done,"

but must involve action and reaction, blow and counterblow, the conflict of forces.

It has become a commonplace of dramatic criticism to say that the Greek tragic differs from ours in that their tragic force was a resistless fate, while with us it springs from recognized antecedents, usually to be found in the voluntary acts of the hero himself. Thus Freytag says:

"The dramatic ideas and the dramatic actions of the Greeks dispensed with a rational world-order, dispensed, that is, with an interlinking of events that is completely accounted for by the conditions and the onesidedness of the characters represented. We are become freer men, we recognize on the stage no other fate than such as arises out of the essential nature of the hero himself."[2]

[1] It is not meant to imply that the three plays were written in sequence or regarded as a trilogy. They were written at long intervals, and probably not in the order of the story, and were not performed together. Cf. Jebb's introduction to his translation of *Antigone*, §§ 22, 23.

[2] *Die Technik des Dramas*, p. 81. And cf. pp. 119–20.

Such phrases are, however, apt to be misleading. Whatever be the difference in the form of statement, the underlying tragic motive in *Œdipus*, and in *Lear* or *Hamlet* or *Othello*, is really the same, namely, "the fatality of the consequences which follow upon every human act."

It has been assumed that much of Ibsen's work is in this respect Greek rather than modern. But even in *Ghosts*, where the idea of an overpowering fate is most prominent, this idea affords the tragic material only, and neither in Ibsen nor in Sophocles is the victim of this "fate" regarded, *per se*, as the tragic hero. In *Ghosts* the victim, Oswald, is not the hero at all — he is a passive sufferer under what the dramatist, mistakenly or not, represents as unalterable law. The real protagonist is Oswald's mother, and the tragic effect is found in the spectacle of her heroic struggle against a power that she finally discovers to be unconquerable.

There is, as has been suggested, a type of tragedy which does not entirely conform to the principles we have been deducing. We have examples of it in Shakespeare's *Richard III*, in Jonson's *Catiline* and *Sejanus*, in Massinger's *The Roman Actor*. In these cases the hero is an absolutely vicious character who holds his place as hero at all only by reason of high intellectual powers. The tragedy presents to us the spectacle of his downfall, it presents the vengeance taken by society upon one who has done violence to all its laws. It does not portray an inner struggle, it does not present a spiritual problem ; it shows the means by which a moral monster is prevented from permanent enjoyment of the fruits of his vices and his crimes.

Such a theme can, it is evident, never be treated so as to attain the highest tragic effect. It may contain much pathos in the subordinate characters — it usually does contain this. When it is great at all its greatness is intellectual solely. It might be better to call this group satiric tragedies, with emphasis on the " satiric," for it possesses the grim irony of satire and its judicial attitude, and thus affiliates with one group of satiric comedy. The differences between *Richard III* and *Sejanus* on the one hand, which are called tragedy, and *Volpone* on the other, which is called comedy, are superficial ; their kinship is essential.

Thus far we have been considering the elements of the tragic in themselves, and, so far as is possible, apart from their effect on the spectator. Aristotle chose the other point of view and defined the tragic solely in terms of its effect.[1] The two elements of this effect he made pity and fear, with a third element which may be here disregarded because, despite the efforts of philosophers and commentators, it is still not quite clear what he meant, nor are we sure that his statement, if we do understand it, is true for us moderns. But pity and fear will be found to be readily convertible into the terms we have used. " Pity " corresponds

[1] *Poetics*, VI.

E

to the suffering and the struggle, "fear" corresponds to the causality. For Aristotle elsewhere distinguishes pity from fear by saying that pity is caused by the perception of suffering which we do not think of as affecting ourselves; fear is caused by the perception of suffering which we realize may be ours. Now this last element is exactly what is involved in causality, it is the element of universal law, whose universality involves us in its sweep, and the perception of which produces, according to our mood, either an enlargement of spirit or a sense of oppression which is probably another name for Aristotle's fear.

Thus we may sum up the elements of tragic effect in three words: suffering, struggle, causality. Suffering alone is pathetic merely; struggle alone may be heroic merely (note the Heracles of Euripides' *Alkestis*); causality alone gives us the rational merely: the union of the three produces the tragic.

CHAPTER V

PERHAPS nothing in the province of literary forms is so baffling as comedy. Considered objectively, as an art-product, it trenches on the realm of the grotesque, confessedly one of the most difficult problems of æsthetics, while in its subjective aspect it requires an analysis of our intellectual processes which has not yet been satisfactorily given us by psychologists. Moreover, in considering concrete literary examples of comedy we are constantly checked by the conviction that the perception of what is comic is something very unstable, subject to change with process of time, and showing wide divergence among different classes of society living at the same time. This is, of course, partly true also of our perception of the tragic, but by no means to the same extent. For tragedy, as we have seen, deals with phases of human nature which are relatively eternal and unchanging. We cannot, of course, affirm that our perception of the tragic in the *Œdipus* is exactly the same as was that of Sophocles' contemporaries; but certainly time has made far less difference here than it has in the understanding and appreciation

of Aristophanes, and this quite aside from the inevitable obscurity of the comic poet's political al-
lusions. Apparently, the feelings to which tragedy
appeals attained a high degree of development at
an earlier time than did those to which comedy
appeals, and they have therefore undergone less
change.

Especially in the last few centuries has the comic
sense been undergoing a modification intimately
connected with the development of that group of
feelings which may be roughly classed as the phil-
anthropic. At the end of the sixteenth century,
the sweetest-natured gentleman of his age could,
without argument, class physical deformity among
the legitimate sources of laughter.[1] To-day such
a sentiment would at once stamp the holder of it
as lacking in fine feeling and sympathetic instincts.
It has only recently occurred to Shakespeare stu-
dents that many of his scenes which to us are tragic
or pathetic were perhaps comic or partly comic to
his audience, and, right or wrong in the given
instances, the suggestion is extremely interesting
as a recognition of the instability of the comic
sense, and as a step toward the study of its evolution.[2]

Such a study is here inadmissible; all we can
do is to recognize that the problem exists, and
admit that what is to be said in this chapter must

[1] Sidney, *Defense of Poesy*, ed. Cook, p. 51.

[2] Cf. John Corbin, *The Elizabethan Hamlet*, and Barrett
Wendell, *William Shakespeare*.

necessarily be subject to modification when the subject shall have been worked out further.

It is generally agreed that the sense of the comic arises from a perception of incongruity. The incongruity may be physical or spiritual, or both; it may be perceptual or conceptual, or both; it may exist in space or in time, or in both; and, according as it is one or another of these, there results one or another variety of comic effect. It may be helpful to make a rough scheme of these classes of comic effects, always remembering that any such scheme can only approximate completeness and only suggest truth.

A. The incongruity is purely conceptual, as in the various forms of wit. Here we may class puns, double meanings, irony, hyperbole, etc. An example is the well-known question, addressed to a servant carrying a roasted hare, "Is that your own hare or a wig?"

B. The incongruity is perceptual as well as conceptual.

I. It is based on a perception of successive events. The source of the comic effect may be stated in general terms as the contrast between expectation and fulfilment. A simple example of this is the case of a man who goes to sit down in a chair, the chair is drawn away, he sits on the floor. Such an occurrence is almost certain to raise a laugh, and the comic in our modern variety show is largely of this character.

In comedy of a higher type, the cases are less

simple, but the principle is the same. The occurrences are partly or wholly in the realm of the intellectual or social, rather than the physical life. Examples of this are the relations between Rosalind and Orlando in *As You Like It*, and the development of the main plots of any of Plautus' or Terence's comedies.[1] These last, however, contain much of the simpler comic, of the variety-show type; so also does Shakespeare's *Comedy of Errors*. The case in *As You Like It*, on the other hand, affiliates with the next group. Indeed, nearly all comedy of intrigue, though its main plot may be reduced to this type, involves some character-treatment, and must therefore be referred in part to the following group.

II. The incongruity is based on a perception of appearances, simultaneous rather than successive. An example is the effect produced by the juxtaposition of a very tall and a very short man, or a very fat and a very thin man. The case is a good one to take, because it is so easily analyzable. The two members of the comparison are here supplied to perception, while a third element — the conception of the normal man — exists in the mind of the percipient as the standard from which both deviate. That this conceptual norm must exist, and must be a norm common to both members of the comparison presented, is shown by the fact that the contrast between a tall man and a child is usually not funny to us, because we

[1] Cf. *infra*, pp. 139 ff.

apply different standards to the two; whereas, if the child attempts to take on a man's ways, he brings upon himself the application of the man's standard, and gets laughed at. Similarly, we laugh when a man adopts a child's manner. Again, the sight of a big tree and a small one side by side is not usually funny, because we have no definitely established standard of size for trees in general. The examples might be multiplied indefinitely, showing the necessity for a common standard, and a definite one.

Starting from these simple cases, we find comic effects ranging all the way up to those of very great complexity. The cases of actual physical deformity, of drunkenness, of the milder forms of insanity, all of which have ceased to be funny to many people, still are highly comic to many, and must be classed here; also instances like the use made of Falstaff's huge size, in *King Henry IV*, or of Ursula's in *Bartholomew Fair*. Our modern comic stage has much of this sort of thing. More complex, but essentially akin, are the cases where the emphasis is laid upon eccentricities of character. The standard applied may be a moral one, as often in Jonson, or an intellectual one, as perhaps in the case of Osric or Polonius in *Hamlet*, or a social one, as in many of Molière's plays. Here we must class all the so-called "Comedy of Humors." Here belong all the effects to which Meredith has exclusively applied the term "Comedy," his standard of reference being the standard of common sense of the well-trained social man considered primarily as in society.[1]

C. There appears to be yet another source of comic effect, which is, however, fortunately growing less and less important. That, namely, which arises from the mere sight of pain, especially pain involving violent movement. To take, as usual, a simple instance, the sight of a man getting a beating is apt to appear funny to some people, even to-day, and any one who reads Aristophanes and Plautus and Terence, or even the Elizabethan and pre-Elizabethan drama, is almost forced to conclude that beatings were esteemed funny *per se*. Of course the comic effect in these cases may often be interpreted as lying not in the beating *qua* beating, but in the beating *qua* surprise, as, for instance, in the *Comedy of Errors*, IV, 4, where Dromio enters, with the rope's end his master had sent him for, and, instead of thanks, gets a taste of it himself. But, placing the most charitable construction on such instances, we are still forced to suspect that, in the comic incident as in case of roast pig, the beating may have helped to "impart a gusto." And this suspicion is strengthened if we note that in all comic surprise the surprise is almost always somewhat disagreeable for the person at whom we laugh, which only means that such comic *dénouements* are, so to speak, beatings in disguise. Perhaps, then, Hobbes was right, at least in his estimate of the natural man, when he

[1] Cf. George Meredith, *An Essay on Comedy*.

calls the comic sense "a sudden glory arising from some sudden conception of some eminency in ourselves by comparison with the inferiority of others, or with our own formerly."

Leaving out of account this last group, which is partly provided for in group *B*, we have two main classes of comic effects, of which the second falls into two parts, according as the contrasts occur simultaneously or successively, and so have to do respectively with plot and with character. But of course, though these groups are separable in thought, they are not so in experience, and the scheme just given makes, we must repeat, no claim to subtlety of discrimination. For in dealing with anything so shifting and elusive as the comic sense, any schematic statement imposing, as it does, hard and fast limits where no such really exist, must of necessity be inadequate and partly false. But it is nevertheless useful if it be taken as merely indicating the main lines of comic effect. It will be found that most literary comedy can be easily put in one or another or in several of the above categories.

The first division, *A*, may be disregarded in this discussion, since it is only incidental in the drama. Group *B*, I and II are essential, as they concern the treatment of life in its two aspects: character (physical or spiritual) and plot. For it is with these that the drama essentially deals.

It is evident that all the cases suggested in the scheme just given have certain things in common ;

they imply a certain attitude on the part of the percipient quite different from the serious or tragic attitude. Every case makes an appeal to the intellect primarily, and to the emotions only secondarily, if at all. The very word "incongruity" implies a process of comparison, which implies the reference to some standard or norm. A fat man is funny, not in virtue of his fatness *per se*, but because most men are not fat. One may ask, "But why is that funny?" which is merely to ask why any incongruity is comic. There is as yet no answer, any more than there is to the question why laughter rather than any other bodily contortion should be the physical expression of amusement. We must take these as ultimate facts, and leave their further explanation to the physiological psychologists.

To return, the whole matter is seen to be dependent on perception of relations and the assumption of a standard of reference.

But further, the incongruity will be perceived as comic only if the attention be held closely to the particular contrast to be made. If it is allowed to wander, to take into consideration other aspects of the subject presented, the sense of the comic may give place to some other feeling. The appeal has thus far been to the intellect merely, and to the intellect working along a narrow and definitely prescribed line. But if the emotions are called in, or if the mind breaks over the prescribed limits of the treatment, the comic incongruity may be forgotten in more serious thoughts.   If, for instance, after smiling at the sight of our very tall man walking beside our very short one, we approach them, and suddenly perceive that the short man is a cripple and deformed, the smile vanishes. Why?   Because a whole set of feelings are called into activity of such a nature and strength as quite to overwhelm the intellectual perception of contrast.   We perceive the contrast, indeed, all the more vividly, but our thought dwells not on the contrast *per se*, intellectually considered, but on what it involves to the cripple himself.   Our emotions are aroused, our sympathy is evoked.

Thus it may be said that the perception of the comic has in it something arbitrary and limited. It requires a point of view which shall cut off from the mental vision the real issues of life and its vital substance,— the emotions and susceptibilities that make it subject to pleasure or pain.   If the view be changed, so as to include these, the comic usually vanishes.[1]   The distinction is one of treatment, of attitude, not of original material, and this is why the same material may be either comic or tragic according to its treatment — why even the same treatment may appear to us comic or tragic according as we fix our attention upon one or another aspect of it; for this reason two people may watch the same occurrence, and one may smile and the other be saddened by it.

[1] But cf. *infra*, p. 65–66.

Take as further illustration an instance from life and one from literature:

A boy stands convulsed with laughter as he watches the wild contortions of two cats whose tails have been wired together; another boy, too small to interfere, may be suffering actual pain at the same sight. What is the difference? In a sense, both boys are right, for, though they are looking at the same occurrence, what they see is not the same: the thing the big boy sees *is* funny; the thing the little boy sees *is* painful. The little boy feels the pain of the tightly wound wire as it cuts into the animals' flesh, he feels the frenzy of the helpless creatures, he resents the brute strength that can willingly cause such tortures. The big boy, on the other hand, simply does not see or feel anything of all this: he sees merely the contortions of the animals, their total failure to comprehend the real cause of their difficulty, and the inadequacy of the means they take to meet it. At the present time society, on the whole, stands with the small boy and condemns the big one; three centuries ago it would have done precisely the reverse; and each position is intellectually explicable though to us only one seems morally justifiable.

Take now an instance from literature:

In *Lear* the subject-matter is the treatment of an old, helpless father by his daughters, and it is so handled as to be one of the most terrible tragedies ever written. But is this the only possible treatment? Turn to Aristophanes, and find in *The Clouds* precisely the same theme made the basis of a comedy — of comedy, indeed, to appreciate which we must divest ourselves of some modern preconceptions, but genuine comedy nevertheless, and not cruel, simply because it is out of the realm of the emotions entirely.

There is, then, this fundamental difference between tragedy and comedy: a difference in point of view — a difference not in the thing as perceived by the eye, but in the thing as conceived by the mind. We may say that tragedy interprets life by emphasizing its vital realities; comedy reconstructs it by emphasizing certain aspects of it, selected so as to make good contrasts, striking incongruities. Each is eminently selective, but the principle of selection is different. And the comic standpoint may be assumed toward almost any subject: it may be momentary, and we have its light playing over the situation for an instant and then going out, as when Hamlet rouses himself from his bitter melancholy to make sport of Polonius or Osric; or it may be pervasive, affecting the entire conception of life as represented by the artist, as in Shakespeare's early comedies (*Love's Labour's Lost, Comedy of Errors*) and Jonson's typical ones; or it may single out certain characters for comic treatment in the midst of an otherwise serious presentation of a subject, as in Shakespeare's later comedies. And according as it is more or less pervasive do we get all the gradations between un-

mixed comedy or pure farce at the one extreme
and the tragedy with comic lights at the other.

To return now to our classification of comic
effects. It has thus far been based on differences
in subject-matter, and we have distinguished the
comedy whose main point lies in the incongruities
of men's character, from the comedy which emphasizes mainly the incongruities in the things
that happen to men. And if *The Comedy of
Errors* is a purer example of the second class than
King Henry IV is of the first, this is because,
dramatically, character can scarcely be presented
save through action, and Aristotle's assertion —
difficult to explain as it stands — is unquestionably
true if we change its application and read: "Without action there cannot be a comedy; there may
be without character."[1]

But in the group of character comedies there is
another basis of distinction. For incongruity of
character implies — it springs from — imperfection
of character. If a man's character were in perfect poise, if it were absolutely symmetrical, it
would not be comic. Comedy, then, is really
based on imperfections in character, but considered from the comic, not the tragic standpoint.

Now it is evident that one may view these imperfections in one of several ways: one may
simply enjoy them as such, without forming a
judgment of the moral or intellectual level of the

[1] Cf. *Poetics*, VI, " Without action there cannot be a tragedy;
there may be without character."

person in whom they are manifested. Or one may, without losing sight of the comic, regard the person with sympathy, or even love. Or one may, consciously or unconsciously, make a judgment, and there is added to our perception of the comic, and modifying this perception, a feeling of superiority, moral or intellectual or both, while we may express this judgment in terms varying from the gentlest irony to the severest condemnation, according to our mood and the nature of the subject. This was the sort of comedy of which Sidney was speaking when he said, "The comedy is an imitation of the common errors of our life, which he representeth in the most ridiculous and scornful sort that may be, so as it is impossible that any beholder can be content to be such a one."[1] The significant thing here is the use of the two words "scornful" and "ridiculous." "Ridiculous" carries with it a notion of superiority on the part of the percipient which is not so palpably implied in other words for the comic; "scornful" still further emphasizes this, leaving out the notion of the comic altogether ; and the concluding phrase of the passage makes the writer's standpoint yet clearer.

Such a passage, especially coming from Sidney, is highly significant. What he would have said if he had lived to see the Shakespearean comedy we can only surmise. Perhaps he might then have seen the possibility of another kind of comic per-

---

[1] *The Defense of Poesy*, p. 28.

ception, wherein we laugh at the folly and love the fool. But, as it stands, the passage fairly represents the type of comedy we have termed judicial.

Jonson's is a stronger statement of the same view:

> " But, with an armed, and resolved hand,
> I'll strip the ragged follies of the time
> Naked as at their birth. . . .
> . . . and with a whip of steel,
> Print wounding lashes in their iron ribs.
>
> . . . .
>
> " . . . Well, I will scourge those apes,
> And to these courteous eyes oppose a mirror,
> As large as is the stage whereon we act;
> Where they shall see the time's deformity
> Anatomized in every nerve and sinew.
>   . . . my strict hand
> Was made to seize on vice. . . . [1]

And Meredith's description of Molière's comedy gives us only another aspect of this kind of comedy:

"Never did man wield so shrieking a scourge upon vice, but his consummate self-mastery is not shaken while administering it. Tartuffe and Harpagon, in fact, are each made to whip himself and his class, the false pietists, and the insanely covetous. Molière has only set them in motion. He strips Folly to the skin, displays the imposture of the creature, and is content to offer her better clothing. . . . The source of his wit is clear reason: it is a fountain of that soil; and it springs

---

[1] *Every Man out of His Humour*, Induction.

to vindicate reason, common sense, rightness and justice." [1]

These two attitudes, the non-judicial and the judicial, though of course neither one is ever adopted with perfect consistency by any given writer, make a convenient basis for distinguishing the two main tendencies of comedy. If we seek for literary types, we shall find the one predominating in Shakespeare, Dickens, George Eliot; the other predominating in Jonson, Molière, Thackeray, Meredith; while Addison and Goldsmith are on the border line between.

We have called the second sort satiric comedy, because its tendency is toward satire. This will be apparent if we make a mental survey of the two fields of comedy and satire, and see how difficult it is at some points to distinguish them. Making Shakespeare one end of the scale, and Juvenal the other, we find next Shakespeare, but with satiric qualities, Addison and Thackeray; close to Juvenal, but with comic qualities, Swift, with Pope and Dryden as subordinate types; between these would come Jonson and Molière, while Aristophanes verges rather on satire, and Rabelais rather on comedy, though a rigid classification of either of these last is beyond possibility.

On the other hand, the pure comedy shades off into other forms. It is, we have said, non-judicial, but one of the reasons why it is non-judicial is because it is sympathetic. Now we have seen

[1] Meredith: *An Essay on Comedy*, pp. 27, 28.

F

that keen sympathy is usually incompatible with comic perception. That it was inevitably and invariably incompatible we expressly did not affirm. For here, as in the case of satiric comedy, there is no hard and fast line drawn, but the two things may shade off the one into the other. We may have the purely comic, where the sympathies, in this sense, are not invoked, as in the Launce episodes of *The Two Gentlemen of Verona;* or as in Sir John Falstaff,— the pure comic preponderating, but enough sympathy so that transition to the pathetic is possible, as hinted in the scene of Falstaff's rebuff at the hands of the young king, and the account of his death.[1] Accentuate the sympathy farther, retaining the comic, and you get Cervantes' comedy; accentuate it still farther and you get the Fool in *Lear.*

Thus we find that the comic sense tends to vary in one of these two directions, — toward the pathetic or even the tragic on the one hand, and toward the satiric on the other. And it is evident that in the case of comedians like Jonson and Molière, who stand part way on the road toward satire, any discussion which does not take into account the satiric as well as the comic aspect must necessarily be inadequate.

One more quality of comedy must be mentioned here, though its purport will be more fully shown

---

[1] *King Henry IV*, Part II, Act V, Scene 5, *King Henry V*, Act II, Scenes 2 and 3. Probably the first of these Scenes was intended by Shakespeare to be comic.

in the chapter on comic plot-structure.   It is this:
comedy, from the arbitrariness, the narrow limita-
tion of its view, leaves out much of life; moreover, the things it leaves out are those things that
we are accustomed to call the serious realities of
life, — the realities of pain and death, and the in-
exorable sway of law.   Hence, comedy is not
bound, as is tragedy, to base itself on law; it may
make a much freer use of what we call chance; the
events and people with which it deals may, if we
may use a figure, all be largely external.   As an
actual fact, comedy does do this, and compared
with tragedy, the emphasis on causality, on law, is
slight.

Summing up: we have seen that comic effects
have a common basis in incongruity, contrast;
that the incongruity may lie principally in the
realm of events, and we have comic intrigue, or in
the realm of appearances, and we have comic character; while usually both these are found in con-
junction, but with preponderating emphasis on
one or the other, which gives us farce or intrigue
comedy on the one hand and character comedy on
the other.   We have seen, too, that comedy differs
from tragedy not so much in subject-matter as in
point of view and treatment.   Finally, we have
noted that comedy itself varies according to the
attitude of the author or the percipient, tending,
where it becomes judicial, toward satire; where it
becomes sympathetic, toward pathos and tragedy.

PART II — TECHNIQUE

CHAPTER I

THE TWO TYPES OF DRAMA

THUS far we have been considering the drama with reference to the general principles which govern it. We have distinguished drama from other literary forms; have considered those qualities which have always been deemed indispensable for good dramatic effect, namely, truth, unity, proportion, seriousness; and have determined, at least in part, what are the essential elements of tragedy and comedy.

Turning now from these fundamental principles, which apply with more or less exactness to other forms of art than the drama, we come to consider in detail the way in which the dramatic form works itself out, — the rules of its technique.

But here, too, before proceeding to those more mechanical regulations which are a part of the craft and are somewhat variable, we ought first to emphasize such laws as are a part of the art and are basic, and therefore permanent.

The serious drama, as we have seen, presents a

struggle between two forces.   Like any struggle, it proceeds from the first repose to the first grappling, then follows the tug and strain of the wrestle, until a moment comes when the advantage begins to go with one side or the other.   From that moment on, the struggle moves inevitably, though perhaps not in a direct line, on to the final overthrow of one of the contestants.   Such is the course of every drama.   The character of the contest may be of various kinds; it may be single combat, — man against fellow-man ; or man against society and social law ; or man against himself; while the sphere of the contest may be in the physical or the spiritual world, or in both.

In any case, the play falls logically into two parts, called the rising and the falling action, whose point of junction and division is this decisive moment just spoken of, called in dramatic terms the climax or turning-point.   In these two parts are set forth respectively the action of the two contestants, the rising action being devoted predominantly to the one that is the aggressor, the falling action to the other.   There are evidently two possibilities: (1) the hero takes the initiative, is the aggressor, or (2) he is in the beginning relatively passive and acts only when he is drawn or driven into action by the attack of the opposing force.   In the first case, the hero is most prominent in the rising action, in the second, he does not come to his fullest expression until the falling action.   Of the first sort, we may take as examples Macbeth, Romeo and Juliet, Richard III, Antigone. Of the second, Othello, more doubtfully, Lear.

Thus in *Macbeth:* in Act I, Scene 3 suggests his aggressive attitude toward his king, and hence toward the political and social law; Scene 4 further emphasizes this; Scenes 5 and 7 clinch his definite determination to kill the king, a determination in which Lady Macbeth is even more prominent than Macbeth himself. In Act II we have the murder of Duncan; in Act III the murder of Banquo. But in Scene 4 of this act, *i.e.* almost the exact mechanical middle of the play, occurs the banquet-scene, which presents the beginning of the reaction in Macbeth's own spirit; in Scene 5 Hecate dooms him with the authority of her magic power; in Scene 6 we have the beginning of the political reaction. (Note the beautiful completeness of this scene-group, wherein the triple reaction — the spiritual, the supernatural, the political — is foreshadowed.)[1] After the banquet-scene Macbeth ceases to have prominence. In Act IV his activity does overlap a little in the murder of Macduff's children, but it is significant that Macbeth himself does not appear here, and the bulk of the act is taken up with the opposition, — hence the elaboration of the scene in Macduff's castle and in the English court between Malcolm and Macduff. In Act V we have a simple working out of the double catastrophe, for Macbeth

[1] Cf. *infra*, p. 83.

and Lady Macbeth, and except for the sleep-
walking scene, the act oscillates between Macbeth
and the insurgent army.[1]

Thus, resuming, we have the first two acts and
half of the third devoted to exposition of the
double hero's activity; the last half of the third
act and all of the fourth and fifth to exposition of
the reaction of this activity. The play illustrates,
with diagrammatic clearness, the essential character of this type of drama.

Compare with this *Othello*. In the first scene
we have the arch enemy, Iago, with his fellow-
conspirator and tool, Roderigo. Their opposition
is stated, and its activity begun. In Scene 2 Iago
is still the central figure, in Scene 3 comes Othello's
great speech before the council, but the scene ends
again with Iago and Roderigo, concerting their
villany:

> " I have't, it is engender'd. Hell and night,
>   Must bring this monstrous birth to the world's light."

In Act II, Scene 1, Desdemona and Othello appear, but are quiet, almost colorless. The illu-
mination is still focussed brilliantly upon Iago,
and the scene closes with his elaboration of his
plan of revenge. Scene 3 witnesses his first decisive move, in working out that part of his scheme
that concerns Cassio. In the first half of Act III
Iago strikes directly at Othello, and the end of this
scene leaves him now in his turn thoroughly

[1] Cf. *infra*, p. 73.

roused, with all his untamable passions inflamed. From this point on Othello receives greater and greater emphasis, though Iago is not allowed to fall into the background. In Scene 4 occurs the first encounter between Othello and Desdemona, which involves the question of the handkerchief. In Act IV, Scene 1, Iago still works up his evidence; Scene 2 has the second interview of Othello with Desdemona, and ends with the plan of Iago and Roderigo for Cassio's death; Scene 3 gives Desdemona her needed prominence. Act V, Scene 1, has the murder of Cassio by Roderigo, which means the perfecting of Iago's plans, but which also ultimately involves his own ruin. Scene 2 has the catastrophe.

Thus it will be seen that, in contrast to *Macbeth*, this play begins by presenting its hero at poise, in a state of repose from which he is not roused until the third act, while from the third act on his passionate activity moves forward in a continuous and tremendous crescendo. Any one who remembers the part as acted by the elder Salvini will remember the overwhelming effect of this crescendo as brought out by the almost brutally titanic power of the actor.

The two types of drama possess each its peculiar advantages and drawbacks, and each makes its different and characteristic impression. In the first, the interest of the audience is more immediately enlisted for the hero, who appears as aggressive and defiant. But the last half of the play is harder to make effective, because the opposing force is apt to be less concentrated and less able to focus the attention. It is, in general, less interesting to see the hero acted upon, than to see him acting. In *Macbeth* we must all feel the weakness of the second half compared with the first, the immediate falling off in effectiveness after the banquet-scene. Yet it was necessary, as we have seen, to set forth the activity of the opposition, and Shakespeare was forced to do this in a series of scenes which tend to scatter the attention and dissipate the interest of the audience. In *Othello*, on the other hand, the interest constantly rises throughout the play, beginning on a low and unemphatic note, and rising through scene after scene to the final clashing chords of the catastrophe. The play can scarcely even be said to have its climax in the third act.[1] It is rather a steady ascent through a series of scenes, each more intense and decisive than the preceding. Possibly, however, it may be said that the contrast with *Macbeth* is not quite fair, because in *Othello* the opposing force is also concentrated in one person, — is embodied in the genius of Iago, — so that it is as if the play had two heroes, one for each half of the action. On this basis the drama might after all be classed with *Macbeth*, because Iago is in one sense the hero, and his activity begins at once. This may be so, but perhaps it only shows that a drama of the highest power will have the strength of each type and

[1] Cf. *infra*, pp. 77–78, and p. 84.

avoid the weakness of each. But, on the whole, the *Macbeth* type has been the one oftenest adopted by the great dramatists. Shakespeare's plays almost all conform to it, and this is one of the reasons why his plays are so often weak in their working out, why the second half often fails to fulfil the promise of the first. It is significant that two of his plays of which this is not true, *Othello* and *Lear*, are of the other type.

In the Greek drama we find both types. To begin with, however, we must remember that the Greek tragedy often leaves out what would be our rising action, and begins somewhere about our turning-point, or even beyond that, in the falling action, at the fourth or fifth act. Thus, when Freytag places the *Œdipus Tyrannus* in the second class with *Lear* and *Othello*, he is using an inapplicable standard. For, to the Greek mind, what went before the written play was also a part of it. Thus, the real plot of the *Œdipus* may be stated, for our purposes, as follows: A young man slays his father and marries his mother, and by this double crime, committed in ignorance, gains possession of a throne. As a result, misfortune descends upon his people, ruin upon him. That is to say, he first acts, boldly and decisively; then he suffers the results of his acts. The parallel with *Macbeth* is apparent, though disguised by the circumstance that whereas the Englishman took his hero at the beginning of his crime and followed him through to the end, the Greek began near the end, presupposing the earlier acts.   The *Œdipus Tyrannus* may be considered as beginning at a point corresponding to the banquet-scene in *Macbeth ;* that proviso made, the correspondences become clear, and the play is seen to be one of the first type.   To class it with *Othello* is to miss its significance.

The *Philoctetes* and the *Ajax* may, however, properly be so classed ; probably, also, the *Electra*. In each of these the hero appears as reacting against forces that have been in long-continued opposition to him.   On the other hand, *Antigone* is plainly of the first type, like *Macbeth* and *Œdipus*, only here there is no difficulty, because the play includes within itself, formally, and not by implication merely, both the deed and the result.

CHAPTER II

LOGICAL DIVISIONS OF THE ACTION

WHATEVER be the disposition of the contesting forces, certain things in the working out are unvarying. There is always a rising action, there is always a falling action, no matter to which of these the chief activity of the hero is relegated; there is always a turning-point and a catastrophe; there are certain other minor but essential elements. It is well to consider these before we take up the more mechanical divisions of acts and scenes, and they will be discussed under the heads: Introduction, Rising Action, Climax, Falling Action, Catastrophe.

And, first, it will be well to look for a moment at the diagram which has, since Freytag presented it, become stock property in dramatic exposition. The play is represented as a pyramid, rising to its turning-point or climax and falling to its catastrophe. The metaphor will be found to be a helpful one. When the climax occurs at about the mechanical middle of the play, the diagram may be made thus (in the diagrams, A = introduction,

B = rising action, C = turning-point, D = falling action, E = catastrophe):

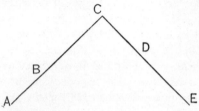

while, according as it falls before or after this point, we may modify the figure thus:

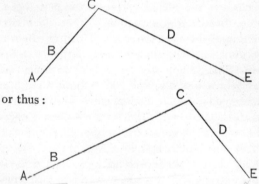

or thus:

indicating in the one case a rapid rising action and a slow descent, and in the other the reverse. *Othello* is, in one interpretation, an example of the last, if we make the steps of the rising action the successive scenes in which Iago arouses and fixes the jealous suspicion of Othello. According to this, Scene 3 of Act III is only one member of the ascent, which rises further in Scene 4 of the same act, and culminates in Act IV, Scene 1. The falling action may be said to begin in the same scene, where Othello, deeming his fears confirmed, first strikes Desdemona. This places the turning-point appreciably beyond the middle of the play, and gives a relatively short and abrupt descent.[1]

[1] *Introduction.* The introduction, whose purpose is to prepare the listener for the play, used often to be set apart from the play itself as a prologue, or given by one of the actors in a set speech. It is by Shakespeare incorporated into the tissue of the play, and forms the first scene, or occasionally a scene-group. There are certain things which it must do, and others which it may do. It must, quickly and deftly, put the hearer in possession of enough facts to make him intelligent in following the play. It must tell him who the speakers are and prepare him for those who are soon to enter; it must at least hint to him the place and time of the action, although this duty is much lightened by the extensive use of scenery on our modern stage. Besides this, it may set the tone of the piece, indicate its "stimmung," thus throwing the sensitive listener into the right mood, much in the same way that the "vorspiel" to some operas does (instance that to *Lohengrin* and to *Parsifal*). But not all dramatic introductions are thus successful. As instances where they are so, may be mentioned the witch

[1] Cf. *supra*, p. 73, and *infra*, p. 84.

scene in *Macbeth*, the scene of the mob in *Julius Cæsar*, of the night watch on the battlements in *Hamlet*, of the street brawl in *Romeo and Juliet*.

It is evident that the management of the introduction is a severe test of the author's skill. He must tell his audience a great deal without seeming to tell them anything. To this end various devices have been employed. We are familiar, on our modern stage, with the chambermaid who vivaciously chronicles the family history as she dusts the family apartment; another resource, often used by the Elizabethans, who had not discovered the chambermaid, is that of the friend just returned from abroad, who must be told all the news. Some such expedient the author is almost forced to employ, even at the risk of seeming "stagey," and few indeed are the plays whose beginnings have not some trace of effort and artificiality; for there is one thing more fatal to a play than artificiality, and that is obscurity. The audience must at any price be made to understand what they are witnessing, and be made to do it with the least possible effort on their part, so that even the boy in the gallery is quite clear in his mind. Under the most favorable conditions, it will always be a rather trying interval, this process of comprehension, and the habitual reader of plays is often conscious of a sinking of the heart as he is confronted with a new set of "dramatis personæ." Many of Shakespeare's beginnings are not wholly successful: instance the first scene of *Hamlet*, whose perfec-

tion is destroyed by Horatio's tedious account to
Marcellus of the political relations of Denmark.
Good beginnings are those of *Macbeth*, I, 2;
Othello, I, 1; the first part of the opening scene
in *Coriolanus;* the whole of the first scene of *Romeo
and Juliet*, and of *Julius Cæsar*. It is an interesting study to go over some of these scenes and
see just how much information we have been given,
which is absolutely needed to understand the play,
and how deftly and without effort this has been
accomplished.

It is almost a rule of the stage that the introduction shall prepare the audience to receive the hero,
but that the hero himself shall not appear. Where
the scene is a long one, this is not so necessarily
the case, and the hero often enters toward its
close (see the opening scene or scenes of *Julius
Cæsar*, *Macbeth*, *Hamlet*, *Othello*, *Romeo and
Juliet*, *Coriolanus*). On the other hand, *King
Lear* plunges at once into the action — for the
few preliminary speeches of Gloucester can
scarcely be counted — since, by good fortune of
the plot and the author's skill in taking advantage of it, there was no need of a preliminary
exposition.

In a few cases, moreover, the hero appears at
once, and the reason for this is easily apparent.
Thus, in *Richard III*, the first monologue of the
king is typical of the way in which his personality
dominates the whole drama. Iago's part in the
first scene of *Othello* may be similarly interpreted,

if we take the play as having a double hero, and
the difference in their respective activities will
account for the introduction of Iago and not Othello
into the first scene.   Compare, too, the different
effect of Marlowe's *Jew of Malta*, where the Jew
himself is at once introduced to us, and Shakespeare's *Merchant of Venice*, where he does not
enter until the second scene.   There is a corresponding difference, which it is hard to think accidental, between the parts played by the two men
in the respective plays, and the attitude of the two
authors toward them.

[2] *Rising Action.* After the introduction comes
the action proper of the play.   It begins with what
is called the "exciting force," that is, the force
which is to change things from their condition of
balance or repose, and precipitate the dramatic
conflict.   From the moment of the exciting force
to the moment of the turning-point, the activity thus
begun, be it that of the hero or of the opposition,
must show a continual, though not necessarily an
even-paced, gain in power and reach.   We have
noted how this continual rise is illustrated by *Macbeth :* the first two scenes form the introduction, and the third scene, Macbeth's meeting with
the witches, furnishes the exciting force.   Here
first is suggested to him the thought that afterwards
develops into act, in the murders of Duncan and
Banquo, while the fulfilment of the first two of the
witches' prophecies, at the end of the same scene,
serves to emphasize their authority.   From this

G

point through to the turning-point we have
a series of scenes, each of which advances the
action somewhat, each carries Macbeth and his
wife more and more irretrievably forward along
the path they have chosen. The only exception
is Act II, Scene 4, which is, also, the only one
which does not bring forward one or both the protagonists. The scene is perhaps introduced to
suggest the beginning of the return action, and,
rather curiously, it is balanced by Act IV, Scene
1, where Macbeth's baleful activity overlaps into
the return action. This is only another instance
of the singularly symmetrical structure of the
play.[1]

But the rising action ought also to introduce the
opposing forces and make the audience familiar
with the characters in which they are embodied,
although it is left for the second part of the play
to give them greater prominence. Thus, the flight
of Malcolm to safety in England hints at a future
opponent to Macbeth; Macduff's refusal to go to
the coronation of Macbeth at Scone is significant;
the failure to kill Fleance suggests the possibility
of further checks; the refusal of Macduff to come
to court emphasizes his hostility already shadowed.
By this means we are prepared for the return action
even before it has actually set in; we are constantly
reminded that this seeming success is perhaps
only strengthening the hand of avenging fate, that
"God is not mocked"; and we are thus, in the

[1] Cf. *supra*, p. 70.

first part, kept from forgetting what in the second part is to be borne in upon us with tremendous force, namely, the universality and inviolability of law.

[3] *Turning-point* or *Climax*.   At a certain point in the rising action a moment comes when the activity of the aggressive force is completed; a moment after which the reversal begins, and there looms into view the force that is to dominate the last half of the action.   This point is the climax, or, better, the turning-point of the play.   It is, of course, possible intellectually to separate this climactic point of the rise from the initial point of the fall, but actually the two moments are often found organically united in the same scene or scene-group. If the play is of the first type, the turning-point will be the moment when the hero completes the accomplishment of his purposes and feels the check of opposition.   Thus in *Macbeth* the banquet-scene begins with the news of Banquo's death, which assures the usurper that his most dreaded rival is removed.   But with the news comes the first check, "Fleance is scaped," and this is followed up by the appearance of Banquo's ghost, foreboding the retribution to come.   The two following scenes may be considered as complementary to this, but they are, very properly, less elaborated, and are transitional to the return action.[1]

[1] Cf. *supra*, p. 70.

In the second type of play, the turning-point shows the converse of this, and represents the hero as passing from a state of relative quiescence to a state of activity. Thus in *Othello* the great scene, III, 3, between Iago and Othello makes the beginning of the turn, though here again we ought perhaps to make a two-membered climax, consisting of this scene plus the first scene of Act IV to the word "Devil!" spoken by Othello to Desdemona, and the blow that goes with it. In a play where the struggle is subjective, and both the contending forces are lodged within the hero himself, the turning-point should be the moment when that force which is ultimately to conquer first gains its decided supremacy. Of this type is Shakespeare's *Antony and Cleopatra*, a play which, however, illustrates dramatic principles as much by their breach as by their observance. Its theme is the struggle between passion and honor, but in the actual working out this theme is obscured by the crowd of unessential details. Its turning-point should come at the point where passion conquers. There are two places where this point might be said to be: first, in Athens, when, after the departure of Octavia as mediator to Cæsar, Antony returns to Egypt and Cleopatra; second, at Actium, when Antony flies, following the galleys of Cleopatra. In Shakespeare's play the first of these two points has been wholly ignored, the second has been very inadequately treated. The battle itself is given to a messenger to describe, and the following scene, III, 2, supremely impressive as its first part is, is not enough.   It would have been right if set in a larger scene-group, like some of the scene-groups in *Hamlet* or in *Julius Cæsar;* but, taken as a single one out of the thirteen scenes of which this act is composed, it is artistically inadequate, out of proportion.   It is, of course, not necessary that the climax be a scene of great outward magnificence, though, in fact, it often is so (cf. *Macbeth, Julius Cæsar*), yet a certain outward impressiveness is, after all, requisite, simply because, as we have seen earlier, the drama deals solely with the phenomenal.   It cannot, as do Ibsen and Mæterlinck in some of their later and more extreme works, deal apparently in commonplaces and expect us to read into these the most supreme spiritual verities.   It cannot, as does Shakespeare in this play, scatter half a dozen superb scenes through a play that has a total of forty-two, and leave the hearer to choose these half dozen to remember.   The dramatist should expect much of his audience, but not so much as this.   He should do his own selecting, his own emphasizing, for herein lies the difference between the raw material and the art-product.

On the other hand, the turning-point or climax must be spiritually emphatic as well as outwardly imposing; the climax in *Macbeth* is not the climax in virtue of presenting a royal banquet with rich, massive effects; that in *Julius Cæsar* is not so in virtue of its impressive massing of

senators assembled in the capitol of the world.
There must be inner significance as well, as in
these cases there is. So, too, the climax need
not be the mechanical middle of the play: it
must be its spiritual centre, the point toward
which it makes from the beginning, and from
which it passes downward to the end.

[4] *Falling Action*. What the exciting force
is to the rising action, that the tragic force is to
the falling action. It is, as we have seen, often
closely united to the climax; sometimes they are,
in a sense, one and the same, as in the *Œdipus
Tyrannus*, where the very announcement that
seems to make him perfectly secure really precipi-
tates the discoveries that end in the catastrophe.
However this may be, the tragic force is the ini-
tiation of the counter activity that is to govern
the second half of the play and bring about the
catastrophe. In *Macbeth*, as we have seen, it is
tripartite;[1] in *Romeo and Juliet* it is dual, being
embodied in the authority of the state and of
Juliet's parents; note that here one of these two
— that of the state — is emphasized before the climax, the other follows immediately upon the climax, being incorporated in the same scene with
it. These two forces are the occasion of the
lovers' ruin — the occasion rather than the cause,
for the causal connection is, after all, indirect,
and if the falling action in the play has a weakness, it is in this fact, — the fact, namely, that the

[1] Cf. p. 70.

forces of the falling action are not the forces that bring about the catastrophe.[1]

If, as is commonly the case, the play is of the first type, and the hero has been prominent in the first half of the play, the falling action will bring forward the characters of the opposition, and the hero will either be in the background, as in *Macbeth*, or, if this is not the case, his treatment will be different, as in *Romeo and Juliet*.

The management of the falling action offers peculiar difficulties. Up to the climax there has been growing suspense. After the tragic force appears, and the development of the opposition has begun, the listener begins to foresee what is to come, his mind naturally plunges forward, and he is impatient if the dramatist's exposition be slower than his own thought-processes. It is like being forced to await the completion of a slowly spoken sentence, whose point we have already anticipated. Perhaps this is the reason why the turning-point and tragic force are often put late in the play, making the actual duration of the return action less than that of the rise. But there is another device for breaking through this over-confident expectancy of the listener. It is the insertion, in the midst of the falling action, of an event which for a moment breaks its advance, seems even to turn it back; there is shown a way of escape for the victim, or at least a jutting crag by which he may delay his fall. This is called the

[1] Cf. *infra*, p. 145.

"final suspense." Instances of it are: the victory of Antony in *Antony and Cleopatra*, IV, 7; the successful carrying out by Romeo and Juliet of all the first part of their scheme; the remorse of Edmund in *Lear*, V, 3, which moves him to revoke his order to kill Lear and Cordelia; the news brought to King Richard in *Richard III*, IV, 4, that the army and navy of his opponents are both scattered; in *Julius Cæsar*, taking the first part as a whole in itself, Cæsar's determination not to go to the senate house that particular day.

Thus the dramatist, having throughout labored to impress upon us the inevitableness of fate, now for a moment reverses his methods and tries to undo all this. But only for a moment; the check has done its duty by keying up the slackened attention, and this done, the action swings back to its true movement and plunges forward to the catastrophe.

[5] *Catastrophe.* We have traced the dramatic struggle through its rise, turning-point, and fall. We now come to its termination. In our ordinary thought, the catastrophe is taken as almost synonymous with death, and this is based on a true conception. For the drama deals with human life, and death is, for the dramatist, the end. It is the fitting conclusion for the tragedy because it really concludes — it is final, precluding possibility of amendment or reprieve.

Evidently, however, its tragic character depends,

not on itself, but upon the nature of the action which it concludes. Death is in itself always solemn, it often moves to pity, sometimes to horror; but it is tragic only when it comes as the natural, the inevitable conclusion of a tragic struggle. And in such cases the death itself will often actually seem a relief, just because it does terminate the struggle, just because it has been felt to be inevitable and so its occurrence relaxes the strain of expectation. This is the case in *Macbeth*. After the horror of the hero's life, its baleful activity without, its moral disintegration within, the physical conflict at the end comes as a return to health. Macbeth himself feels it. After the first sinking of heart that comes with the loss of his last support, there follows the rebound, the natural, if desperate joy in a fair fight, and there is a ring of freedom in his last defiance:

> " Lay on, Macduff,
>   And damn'd be he that first cries, Hold, enough ! "

Similarly, Brutus certainly feels death to be a release as he says:

> "Cæsar, now be still :
>   I killed not thee with half so good a will."

In *King Lear* the consummation of the tragedy is, it is true, in a death; not, however, Lear's death, but Cordelia's, and this is tragic, not as it concerns Cordelia, but as it touches Lear himself. The climax of "pity and fear" is in the sight of the mad old man, with the strength of despair, carrying in his dead daughter to show to all men,— the sight of him as he holds the feather to her lips to reveal her breathing, and, dim-eyed in the flesh, sees, with the vision of fevered desire, faint tokens of life. The tension breaks, and he dies, but his death is not tragic. It completes the tragedy of his life, and is fit, right, necessary; but for him it is a release. Kent's feeling is ours:

"Vex not his ghost: O, let him pass! he hates him much
That would upon the rack of this tough world
Stretch him out longer."

But death is often, too, the consummation of the tragedy in another way. In *Antigone*, the young girl's death is the tragedy, because it marks the completeness of her subjugation to crushing human law; whereas the deaths of Hæmon and of Eurydice, in so far as they are tragic at all, are so not in themselves, but in their effect on Creon. In *Romeo and Juliet* the deaths of the two lovers constitute the tragedy because only thus is forever shut off the possibility of recovered happiness.

What the catastrophe must bring about is not primarily death, but finality — an equilibrium of forces which shall convince us of its permanence. It may be compared to the crash of the landslide by which the too precipitous cliff regains a natural slope. In *Julius Cæsar* there may be said to be two points of catastrophe: the first for Cæsar, the second for the conspirators. In the first half of the play, Cæsar falls because he had risen too high; Brutus and Cassius, representing the norm, pull him down. But then they in their turn rise too high, and the second half of the play shows how they are therefore in their turn overthrown.

In the management of the catastrophe, more than anywhere else, there should be concentration, both of thought and expression. During the earlier part of the play, much elaboration is possible, much incident, much working-up of character and episode; but as we near the close the lines should narrow. Earlier, many outcomes were possible; now nothing is possible except the single end to which everything has been tending. Upon this the rays must all converge, everything subsidiary must be eliminated. And if the drama has been well motived and well constructed, there will be no need for elaboration, or even for much emphasis. The end is inevitable, all it requires is bare statement. To give more than this, to attempt explanation and commentary, implies carelessness on the part of the author, or a lack of faith in his work. Of carelessness, we have an illustration in the last lines of *Julius Cæsar*, the conversation between Messala, Strato, and Octavius, concerning the promotion to favor of Brutus' servant. It is a petty detail, that spoils the simple greatness of the close. In another way, the concluding lines, given to Octavius, will, to some of us, seem another dissonance. The play naturally ends with Antony's words, "This was a man," and we would

fain rest here.   Octavius' cold words point forward into a new realm of life, and at the moment
when we ought to feel that all is finished, we are
reminded of the political rearrangements to come,
the division of spoil — things which are histori-
cally true enough, but which are here not fitting.
Perhaps it was Shakespeare's optimism that moved
him to make this sort of mistake as often as he
did, but if so it was optimism ill-timed.

Summing up: we find that the action of the
drama falls naturally into two parts, a rise and a
fall; that the rising action has four parts: the
introductory exposition, the exciting force, the
working out, and the climax or turning-point.
The falling action has three parts: the tragic
force, the working out, and the catastrophe, while
often the final suspense makes a fourth part.

Often, however, dramatic critics make a three-
fold division instead of a twofold, namely, into
the rising action, the climax, and the falling
action.   But if the climax is organically developed out of the rising action, as it ought to be,
it is organically a part of it and should not be
separated from it, even in thought.

These, then, we have called the essential elements of the drama, in distinction from those
mechanical divisions, called acts and scenes, of
which the dramatic structure is made up.

CHAPTER III

(1) *The Acts*

WE have called the division of the play into acts and scenes a mechanical one, in distinction from the logical division which has just been discussed. The single fact that the five acts of a play are commonly of about equal length would make it antecedently improbable that they should correspond to the organic articulation of the action's parts. That they actually do not so correspond will be evident from the most superficial inspection of any play. For the first act does not cover the introduction alone; the second act does not suffice to contain the rising action, which begins in the first act and overlaps into the third; the third act almost always contains the climax, but it also includes the penultimate stages of the rising action and the initial stages of the falling action; the main part of the falling action is contained in the fourth act, but its last part runs over into the fifth act, which is therefore not exclusively devoted to the catastrophe.

The relation between the mechanical and the

logical divisions of the play may be thus diagrammed :

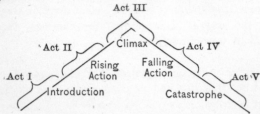

It might seem, then, that the acts have no organism in themselves — that they are merely marked
off with a tape at equal distances in the course of
the play. This is not altogether the case. The
division into acts is indeed somewhat a matter of
stage convenience: it gives the audience time to
relax, and the actors time for rest or for change of
costume, it furnishes opportunity for extensive
scene-shifting. Moreover, from the author's point
of view it is useful because it gives him a few points
in the action wherein, the continuity being completely broken, he may assume greater changes and
longer lapses of time than is advisable between
scenes.

But each act ought to be, to some extent, a
whole in itself; it ought to have a "beginning,
middle, and end," a rise and fall somewhat like
the rise and fall of the drama as a whole. In the
Greek tragedy the sections of the action falling
between the choruses formed such wholes, while
in the Senecan tragedies, whence modern drama

took its formal five-act structure, each act is distinctly complete in itself. In the *Medea*, for example, the five acts present each a distinct stage of the action. Disregarding the choruses, they may be thus epitomized:

Act I. Presents Medea's turbulent mood as she realizes that she is about to be deserted by her husband.

Act II. Stirred by the bridal chorus, she meditates revenge, but does not yet determine on whom it shall fall. In order to perfect and carry out her yet immature plans, she obtains leave to remain in the palace one day longer.

Act III. Her anger increases and hardens into cold resolve. In an interview with Jason she assures herself that he really loves the two children he has had by her. She therefore decides to kill them, as well as Creusa, his new bride.

Act IV. She invokes the aid of magic to endow with destructive powers the rich gifts she purposes to send to Creusa. Her incantations finished, she sends the gifts by her sons.

Act V. A messenger announces that Creusa and her father have died in agony, and that the city is in flames. Medea, rejoicing in this first fruit of her vengeance, proceeds to complete it. One of her sons she kills before his father arrives, the other she kills in Jason's presence. She herself departs in her magic chariot.

It will be seen that each act makes one step in the course of the action, each is dominated by a distinct mood in Medea herself: in the first act, it is half-dazed surprise and anger; in the second, wild rage and fierce longing for vengeance; in the third, hard and deliberate resolve; in the fourth, the elation of conscious power; in the fifth, exultation in completed vengeance, alternating with horror at her own deeds.

Each act, moreover, besides completing its section of the action, points forward, at its close, to the action that is to follow. Thus at the end of Act I comes her dark prophecy that, as through crime she entered the house of Theseus, through crime she will leave it. At the end of Act II this is made more definite when she gains the day's reprieve in which to work out her vengeance. At the end of Act III she suggests the details of the plot she is to carry forward in the next act. At the end of Act IV she sends the fatal gifts, and we wait for Act V to learn the result.

Turning now to the modern drama, we find that the structure of the classic French plays is closely similar to their Senecan models. But with Shakespeare the case is different. Of no one of his plays can such an epitome as the one just given possibly be made. The acts have no such unity; instead of presenting a single step in the action, a single mood in the protagonist, they are a network of activities, a complex of moods.

Yet in some cases a kind of unity is discoverable. This is especially true of *Macbeth*. Here, the first act shows Macbeth yielding to the evil promptings of ambition, while Duncan's visit gives him the opportunity to follow out his desires. The second act centres about the murder of Duncan. The third act presents the consummation of Macbeth's plots and the beginning of the reaction. The fourth and fifth acts, which are, as is usual with Shakespeare, not so well constructed, present the preliminary and the final stages of the reaction. Take now, in greater detail, the third act:

SCENE I. As a kind of introduction, Banquo sums up Macbeth's course hitherto:

> "Thou hast it now: King, Cawdor, Glamis, all
> As the weird women promised; and, I fear,
> Thou play'dst most foully for 't — "

PART I. Then his mind reverts to the part of the witches' oracle which has concerned himself. This second thought strikes the keynote of the act, since it is the memory of that prophecy which leads Macbeth to plan Banquo's murder.

PART 2. The court enters, and Macbeth enjoins Banquo to be back for the night's feast. His emphasis on Banquo's return — "fail not our feast," "Adieu, till you return at night" — points forward with double irony, first, to the measures Macbeth is about to take that Banquo may *not* "return at night," and, second, to the terrible manner in which the murdered man is, after all, to fulfil the king's injunction.

H

PART 3. Then follows the interview between the king and the murderers, really a scene in itself, with its own introduction (lines 73–85), rise (86–115), climax (116–126), and conclusion.

Thus the scene falls into three parts, an introduction, a transitional part, and a last part forming the first link in the rising action of the act.

SCENE 2. This scene is chiefly of value as character-exposition. It does not advance the story. The opening words again insist, like the repetition of a theme in music, upon the Banquo motive:

> "*Lady Macbeth.* Is Banquo gone from court?
> *Servant.* Ay, Madam, but returns again to-night."

Then follows the interview between Lord and Lady Macbeth, giving the necessary insight into their desperate moods. The phrases, "these terrible dreams that shake us nightly," "the torture of the mind," "life's fitful fever," "O, full of scorpions is my mind," are needed to give the spiritual atmosphere of the act. The scene ends by reverting to the theme with which it began.

SCENE 3. The murder of Banquo. The escape of Fleance is the first check to Macbeth's plans.

SCENE 4. The banquet-scene. It is in three parts:

The brilliant introduction emphasizes the king's royal state. The few words with the murderer serve to set Macbeth's mind at rest as to the success of his plot against Banquo.

With the entrance of the ghost the change

comes, and there follows the half-crazed agony of the king, and the hurried breaking up of the banqueters.

The last few lines of the scene sketch the after-mood of the king, varying between remorse and a feverish and desperate resolution.

This scene is, of course, the climax of the act, as of the play. It presents the consummation of the king's plans and the beginning of the reaction. If we seek a turning-point in a few lines, we might find it in these, where he seems dimly conscious of the nemesis to come:

> "the time has been,
> That, when the brains were out, the man would die,
> And there an end: but now they rise again,
> With twenty mortal murders on their crowns,
> And push us from our stools."

SCENE 5. The witches and Hecate plan to draw on Macbeth "to his confusion."

SCENE 6. The two lords hint their suspicions with regard to Macbeth, and speak of the party Macduff is raising for resistance.

Thus the act has a regular rise and fall. It rises to the murder of Banquo, the escape of Fleance suggests the turn, while the banquet-scene and the two following scenes develop the three-fold character of the reactionary forces, the forces, namely, of the moral order, of the supernatural realm, and of the political world.

In *Lear*, Act III, there is, considering the complicated nature of the double plot, a fairly

LEAR-PLOT.

GLOUCESTER-PLOT.

Sc. 1.
Introductory.
Heath. Storm.

Sc. 2.
Rise.
Lear Enters,
mad.

Sc. 3.
Introductory.
Gloucester and
    Edmund.

Sc. 4.
Climax.
Hovel-Scene.

Sc. 5.
Rise.
Edmund betrays
    Gloucester to
    Cornwall.

Sc. 6.
Secondary Climax and
    Fall.
Trial-Scene : Lear
    Carried out for
    Dover.

Sc. 7.
Climax.
Blinding of Gloucester.
Wounding of Cornwall
    hints a return-action.

compact structure.   For the Lear-plot the act may be considered as extending from Scene I to Scene 6; for the Gloucester-plot, from Scene 3 to Scene 7.   Making a double order, we may sketch it as in the accompanying diagram.

It is to be noted that the treatment of the two plots is in this act different in kind: that of Lear is expository, that of Gloucester is narrative.   The first has its expository climax in the hovel-scene, it falls away in the gentler tone of the farm-house scene, ending in the old king's exhausted sleep; the second has a steady rise through the three scenes, culminating in the blinding of Gloucester, and having an abrupt fall in the wounding of Cornwall.

But such cases of good act-structure are not to be taken as typical of Shakespeare.   In *Lear*, for example, the other four acts are, in this respect, hopelessly inorganic.   *Macbeth* is more evenly good, though the first three acts are the best.   It is noteworthy, too, that where, as in *Lear*, one act surpasses the others in structural compactness, it is the third.   Now the third act has for its nucleus the climax of the play as a whole, and it can thus hardly help having a well-marked rise and fall.   However, an act may be well constructed and not have both rise and fall — everything depends on what is its position in the play. Take the first two acts of *Macbeth;* Act I may be thus summarized:

SCENE 1. Witches. Introductory — suggests the "tone" of the play.

SCENE 2. Camp. Introductory exposition.

SCENE 3. Witches, Macbeth, and Banquo. Exciting force.

SCENE 4. Duncan, his generals, etc. Exciting force strengthened by partial fulfilment of the witches' prophecies, which increases Macbeth's confidence in them.

SCENE 5. Lady Macbeth resolves on the murder of Duncan. This initiates the rising action.

SCENE 6. Duncan received by Lady Macbeth.

SCENE 7. Lady Macbeth strengthens Macbeth's resolution.

Here the first scene is merely preliminary — like the striking of chords in music; the second is introductory; the third and fourth present the exciting force; the fifth, sixth, and seventh present the first stages of the rise. The act is perfectly compact and ends at exactly the right moment.

Compare now Act II.

SCENE 1. Expositional of Macbeth's highly wrought state.

SCENE 2. Contrasting sketch of Lady Macbeth's mood. Macbeth enters, having done the murder. The knocking on the gate.

SCENE 3. The discovery of the murder. Flight of Malcolm and Donalbain.

SCENE 4. Ross and Macduff discuss the murder. Macduff will not attend Macbeth's coronation.

The act, in contrast with the preceding, has a rise and fall: it works up to the murder and presents the beginning of the reaction from the deed as shown on Macbeth and on those about him. Taken in greater detail, it has two points of supreme tension: the first in Scene 2, the second in Scene 3. The first part of Scene 1, the talk between Banquo and Macbeth, is skilfully managed so as to be pregnant with suggestion. Banquo's frank remark, "I dreamt last night of the three weird sisters," recalls the theme of the rising action, while Macbeth's quick, guilty answer, "I think not of them," is in marked contrast. There follows Macbeth's soliloquy — really a separate scene, and paralleled by the soliloquy of Lady Macbeth at the beginning of Scene 2. After Macbeth enters, having killed Duncan, the first point of tension is reached; when the knocking commences there is a sudden relaxing. The porter's entry makes a break, then the second rise begins, culminating in the discovery of the murder. From this point the tension relaxes again.

Thus the movement of this act is seen to be quite different from that of the preceding one, and yet different from Act III. If they were to be symbolized in diagrams, they would be about as follows (the Roman numerals indicate acts; the Arabic, scenes):

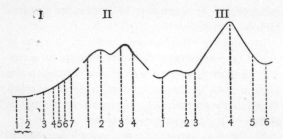

One more point is to be noted. It was seen in the *Medea* of Seneca that each act had toward its close some suggestion of the action that was to follow in the next. The same thing may be observed at the end of almost any of the acts in Shakespeare's plays. Of the three acts just analyzed, the first closes with the criminal resolve of Macbeth and his Lady; the second has the scene with Macduff, which is subtly suggestive of his antagonism to Macbeth; the third blocks out the three main forces of the return action.

One might multiply instances of such secondary, anticipatory rise. A notable exception is found in *Romeo and Juliet*, in the position of the street brawl scene, wherein Tybalt is killed. We should expect it at the end of Act II instead of at the beginning of Act III. It would have given exactly the note of warning needed to intensify the scenes of the climax, yet would not have trenched so closely upon these scenes. The third act would then have begun with the orchard scene, and would have gained the jewel-like unity that is the concomitant of singleness of impression in complexity of material.

In studying act-structure, however, it must of course be remembered that the absence of a curtain made the divisions between the acts much less marked then than now. Yet the case of *Macbeth* shows that structural act-unity could be, though it seldom was attained by Shakespeare.

The fact is, we must not expect from Shakespeare perfection of structure. In seeing and seizing upon the essential dramatic moments in his theme he was almost unerring, but in the working out he was usually careless — possibly he was really indifferent, conscious that he possessed the "one thing needful." Certainly the attempt to deduce laws from his act-structure gives, in the main, only negative results, whereas a study of the dramatic moments — what we have called the logical divisions — of his dramas is exhaustlessly fruitful.

Our modern drama has a character intermediate between the French seventeenth century and the English Elizabethan and Stuart drama. Each act has greater complexity than had the French, greater compactness than the English. Ibsen, in so many respects affiliated with the Greek drama, usually preserves the unity of place and sometimes that of time, as in *Ghosts*, and each act is individual in its presentation of some phase of the theme. Sudermann's dramas are models in cleanness of construction, and they have the effectiveness that comes of masterly technique. In Wildenbruch's *Heinrich und Heinrich's Geschlecht*, his latest and perhaps his strongest drama, the act-structure is remarkably compact. The play is built up about the humiliation of the emperor at Canossa and is in two "evenings," each forming a play by itself, of which the first is the more powerful. An analysis of its acts makes an interesting contrast with the Shakespearean form. It has a prologue and four acts.

PROLOGUE. This shows Heinrich when a boy of ten. It serves to give an insight into his original, unperverted nature, and thus to invoke the sympathies of the audience.

ACT I. The State House in Worms. King Heinrich returns from a victorious campaign against the rebellious Saxons. Messengers from the Pope arrive, refusing to grant his request for the emperorship, and censuring him for his evil courses. He sends back a message of defiance couched in studiedly insulting terms. The act is chiefly expositional, presenting the two great factors in the struggle that is to ensue, namely, the king's intense love for his people and the radical antagonism between his nature and ideals and those of the Pope.

ACT II. There are two scenes, the first in Rome, the second in Worms.

SCENE 1. Pope Gregory is giving judgment on the penitents brought before him. Heinrich's defiance reaches him. He wavers between the dictates of wordly ambition and those of the spiritual vision.

SCENE 2. Heinrich is under the Pope's ban, but bitter and unyielding. The children of Worms come out with Christmas gifts for the little prince, his son. Softened by this evidence of their love, Heinrich resolves for their sakes to humble himself before Pope Gregory, and secure tranquillity for his people.

ACT III. Canossa.

SCENE 1. An audience room in the castle. Gregory is beset by the Saxon faction, enemies of Heinrich, who offer to depose him and let the Pope create an emperor who shall be a tool of the church. As Gregory wavers before the temptation to grasp at temporal power, it is announced that King Heinrich has come to do penance.

SCENE 2. Another audience room. After three days of struggle with conflicting motives, Gregory admits the royal penitent and recalls his curse. Heinrich, at the height of spiritual exaltation, learns of the Pope's dealings with the Saxons, and the perception of this double dealing shatters his faith. His mood changes to one of hard cynicism, and he leaves the presence determined to gain the emperorship by force of arms.

ACT IV. Rome. A fortified tower where the Pope has taken refuge. Heinrich enters the city with his army. In disguise, he visits Gregory and asks him to crown him emperor. Gregory refuses, and Heinrich goes, to set up a new pope who shall do his will. Gregory dies, while from below are heard the cries of the populace, "Emperor Heinrich and Pope Vibert!"

From this epitome it will be seen how each act presents one phase of the subject treated. The first suggests the factors in the problem; the second presents the two great protagonists, Heinrich and Gregory, showing how each is torn by conflicting impulses; the third brings the problem to its issue; the fourth presents the provisional solution, which the second part of the play is to bring in question, but which affords temporary stability.

Among modern French work, an example of beautiful act-structure is Edmond Rostand's *Cyrano de Bergerac*, which, though called a "heroic comedy," has a partly tragic theme and the structure of serious drama. It has five acts, each located in a single place: the first, at the Hotel de Bourgogne; the second, at Rageneau's bakery, a rendezvous for Bohemian Paris; the third, a street before a house; the fourth, a camp at the siege of Arras; the fifth, a convent garden. Each act is a wonder of construction, being highly complex in material, yet close-knit, with no tendency to straggle or fall apart. The first two acts have each a central climax, with a secondary rise toward the close, anticipatory of the following act. The third act has the central climax, but the secondary one is less marked. The fourth act is constructed like a fifth act, with a central climax and a sudden fall to a catastrophe; but the curious double nature of the hero's activity makes this conclusion only partial, and the brief fifth act is needed for the final resolution.

Summarizing: the division into acts has been called mechanical, in distinction from those logical divisions that are grounded in the development of the theme itself. In the Senecan drama, however, and in the classic French drama modelled thereon, each act has a lyric unity not found in the freer, more epic English drama. The best of the modern work combines the complexity and variety of the English manner with the more careful form of the French.

(2) *The Scenes*

The word "scene" has several meanings. It may denote merely the place in which the action occurs; it may refer to the entrances and exits of the persons; or it may mean such a section of the play as, in virtue of its significance, constitutes a unit in the treatment. According to French usage, any change in the number of persons on the stage, either by addition or diminution, makes a new scene. In common English usage, a new scene is indicated when the stage has been cleared and a new entrance occurs. The place of the action may or may not be changed. Thus, in *Macbeth*, Act II, the first three scenes occur in the same place, a court of the castle. The first scene would, according to French usage, be three scenes: one with Banquo and Fleance; one with Banquo, Fleance, and Macbeth; one with Macbeth alone. It is in our editions indicated as a single scene, because the entrances and exits overlap; but between Macbeth's exit and the entrance of Lady Macbeth the stage is clear, hence a new scene is made. Either method of division has drawbacks. The French method often gives importance to an exit or an entrance — that of a servant, for instance — which does not make a real break in the action, and almost always there will be several, sometimes a dozen, of these little, mechanical scenes, going to make up what we may call the logical scene — that is, the scene which develops one phase of the subject. On the other hand, the English method sometimes leaves unemphasized an entrance or an exit that is of great importance, and we have really two logical scenes in one mechanical one. Thus in *Macbeth*, Act III, Scene 1, there are three distinct parts: (1) Banquo alone, (2) Banquo, Macbeth, and the court, (3) Macbeth and the murderers.

When, therefore, we say that the scene should have in little what the act and the play has in large, — a compact, organic structure with a "beginning, middle, and end," — it is of the logical, not the mechanical scene that we are speaking.

If Shakespeare is weak in act-management, he is strong in scene-management. Perhaps this is because the scene is small enough to be kept in view as a whole, even by the careless and rapid worker that Shakespeare often was; but, whatever be the reason, one may choose almost at random and find a scene exhibiting fine technique.

As in the case of the act, so in the scene the rise and fall has not always the same form. Act II, Scene 3, of *Macbeth* has a central rise, but Scene 1 rises toward the close, Scene 2 falls toward the close, and the three scenes, following Freytag's method, might be thus diagrammed:

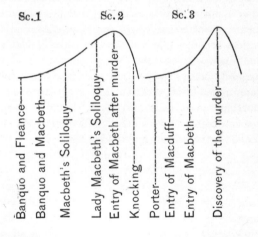

and Scenes 1 and 2 ought, logically, to be taken either as four scenes or as one great scene in four parts, for Macbeth and his wife count here as one person, and their two soliloquies are complementary parts of the continuous rise to the murder itself.

In some ways, the words "rise" and "fall" are not helpful, however, and it almost seems unfortunate that Freytag imposed them on dramatic criticism. They are purely figurative, and figurative expressions are misleading when allowed to harden into formulas. As just used, they referred to the tension of the actors in the scenes, and hence of the audience as it follows the action. Thus Scene 1 begins quietly, with Banquo's words to Fleance, the conversation with Macbeth has more tension, and the soliloquy reaches a spiritual tumultuousness that goes over, on the same pitch, though with difference of tone, into the next scene, and increases on Macbeth's reëntry after the murder. The knocking on the gate acts like a dash of cold water: it breaks the continuity of mood and produces a sudden relaxation of tension.

For another instance of good scene-structure, take *Romeo and Juliet*, Act III, Scene 1:

INTRODUCTION. Benvolio and Mercutio by their casual talk prepare us for what is to follow:

> "The day is hot, the Capulets abroad,
> And, if we meet, we shall not scape a brawl."

EXCITING FORCE. Tybalt and other Capulets enter ; a dispute arises between Tybalt and Mercutio.

RISE. Romeo enters, bears Tybalt's insults, and tries to calm him.

First Climax. Fight between Tybalt and Mercutio, Mercutio mortally wounded. The news of Mercutio's death overcomes Romeo's self-control.

Second Climax. Reëntry of Tybalt. Romeo defies him, they fight, Tybalt is killed.

Return and Resolution. Entry of the populace, with Montagues, Capulets, and the prince. The guilt of Romeo's action is argued, the prince decides against him and banishes him.

The scene, with its two climaxes, might be thus diagrammed:

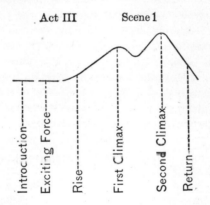

In the above scene, the words "rise" and "fall" have regard not only to the inner excitement of the participants, but to the outer events that advance the story.

In other cases the entire scene is broad exposition of spiritual states. Thus, in *Lear*, Act III, Scene 4, we have an elaborate study of the old man's madness. The beginning is quiet, but by the end of his first long speech the king has worked himself up to an excitement whose character he himself recognizes:

> "O, that way madness lies; let me shun that;
> No more of that."

He becomes outwardly calm again, but the entry of Edgar feigning madness brings before his eyes the very madness he fears for himself, and perhaps draws him on toward it. At all events, his excitement grows again until it reaches the frenzy in which he cries, "Off, off, you lendings! come, unbutton here," and tears away his clothes. This is the point of greatest spiritual tension in the scene. Gloucester's entrance makes a break, and brings to the front Edgar, whose feigned ravings drop to the whimpered refrain, "Poor Tom's a-cold," "Tom's a-cold," while Lear's fury subsides to a dazed quietude. Here the words "rise" and "fall" refer wholly to the spiritual intensity of the scene.

Summing up: the play, as a whole, is like an organism: it is articulated into acts, which are in turn articulated into scenes. Each act and each scene has its own individual completeness — a completeness which is, however, subordinated to that of the whole of which it forms a part. The scenes fall naturally into larger or smaller groups, and cannot be considered out of their position without in some fashion having violence done them.   Each scene, regarded as a unit in a greater whole, resembles not one brick in a straight wall, but one stone in an elaborate arch: the form of the stone will be determined by the point in the arch at which it is placed and the purpose — whether this be ornament or support — which it serves.

CHAPTER IV

CHARACTER-TREATMENT

IN the serious drama, it is impossible to consider plot wholly apart from character or character apart from plot. At least, this ought to be so, for the plot being grounded in causality, not accident, its action is the inevitable outgrowth of the characters concerned in it. Hence, in dealing with dramatic principle and with plot-structure, much has been already stated or assumed with regard to the tragic hero. In fact, all the essentials have been thus stated or assumed. He must, we have seen, have the freedom that both develops the positive, the " royal " character, and offers it opportunity for initiative; he must, we have assumed, possess strength of some sort, otherwise he will not hold his own for a moment in the tragic struggle — rather, no tragic struggle would be possible; but his nature will be one in which conflicting tendencies and impulses are present, for in these conflicting tendencies lies his weakness and the opportunity and occasion for the tragic conflict itself. Finally, all these requirements usually imply that he will be a man of eminence, either by birth or fortune or training, and

that he will have the power of self-expression, enabling us to understand the inner life that is not adequately represented in action. Thus much is evident with regard to the hero of the tragedy or the serious drama, and it is true of the other characters in proportion as their activity in the play resembles his.

Aristotle laid it down as a general rule, that the hero should be neither wholly bad nor wholly good, because in the one case the spectacle of the hero's suffering would not move our pity, in the other it would simply shock us.[1] Yet the philosopher had before him the example, in *Antigone*, of a faultless heroine, in whose judgment of herself we concur: "I shall rest, a loved one with him whom I have loved, sinless in my crime."[2] Possibly Aristotle did not admit this play as on a level with the *Œdipus* in tragic power; certainly it has no parallel. For Shelley's Beatrice, it is true, feels that her crime is the only right thing, but though her heart is the heart of Antigone, her choice is an Orestean one, from either of whose alternatives there is an instinctive recoil.

Setting aside, for a moment, this single case, consider these requirements as to goodness and badness in the hero. There are reasons for them deeper than those given by Aristotle.

We saw that the drama meant struggle, either with outer forces or, as in almost all the greatest

[1] *Poetics*, XIII.
[2] *Antigone*, trans. Jebb, p. 23.

dramas, with inner forces. If the struggle is an inner one, it means a divided soul with a divided allegiance, conflicting impulses. Such is the case with Orestes, with Hamlet, with Lear, with Beatrice, with Brutus, with Wallenstein, with Faust, with Strafford. None of these has either, on the one hand, the steadfast poise and invulnerability that we associate with perfect goodness, like that of Christ or the mythical Socrates; or, on the other hand, the assured firmness and security of another sort that we associate with absolute and deliberate badness, like that of Richard III as conceived by Shakespeare. But neither Christ nor Socrates would lend themselves to treatment as a tragic hero, and Sudermann's latest drama, *Johannes*, which attempts a tragic treatment of John the Baptist, does not encourage efforts to use this type of character. Shakespeare's use of the opposite type, in *Richard III*, results in a play of tremendous power, but, as we have seen, the play is not tragedy at all in the sense in which we have been using the term. Similarly, in Jonson's *Sejanus*, the two central characters, Claudius and his great favorite, are both monsters of vice and wickedness, but here again the result is not true tragedy, for such characters leave no room for tragic struggle and tragic suffering, and this drama must be placed, with *Richard III*, in a class apart. With these belongs Massinger's *The Roman Actor*, though in this case the central character, Nero, has, for the purpose of tragic effect, been considerably softened by the dramatist: his passionate devotion to his crime-won wife — a devotion which, so far as the limits of this drama are concerned, is single and absolute — carries him out of himself, and renders him vulnerable in a sense that is not true of Richard or of Sejanus.

Returning now to *Antigone*, it must, first of all, be said that this drama has in it a larger element of the pathetic than, for example, *Hamlet*, or the tragedies dealing with Orestes, and that this is due to the fact that she is preëminently the victim of outer misfortune. Moreover, we feel the tragic element in her story in proportion as we realize that she also has been the battlefield of contending forces; that, calm though she appears, she has had a conflict, whose bitterness is hinted in her last outburst of longing for the life and joy she has given up. But her case is different from that of Macbeth or of Hamlet, since the necessity of the conflict has been imposed upon her from without, instead of arising from within,— such was, until Euripides, the phase of tragic conflict chiefly emphasized in Greek drama.

Evidently, the exceptional case of *Antigone* only helps to establish the rule that tragedy is to be found, not in suffering merely, but in suffering accompanied by struggle. In so far as *Antigone* shows the suffering without the struggle it is not tragic but pathetic, as will appear yet more clearly if the play be compared with *The Cenci* and with the dramas whose subject is the story of Orestes.

We find, then, the plays *Antigone* and *Richard III* at the two ends of the scale, but each on the boundary line of typical tragedy, though not for the reason that Aristotle gives. For the question is not one of goodness or badness as such, and it is darkening counsel to bring these elements into the discussion. The drama deals with men, not devils or angels, and this not because devils are bad and angels good, but because both are fixed and out of the range of passion, outside of the life that is the dramatist's sphere. The drama shows men stirred to the foundations of their being, open to influence, capable of change, torn by desires, able to be aroused to the most intense activity, emotional, intellectual, volitional ; and such men have the souls neither of devils nor angels, but are a compound of elements from both.

So much for the character of the tragic hero considered in itself. Consider it now with regard to the dramatist's presentation and the spectator's appreciation of it.

Given a vital, positive character, given freedom to show his individuality in action, the thing that is above all necessary in the treatment is the arousing of the spectator's sympathy. He must be made, not merely to see the acts, but to sympathize with their motiving. If the fact is a murder, we must ourselves feel the feelings that lead up to the deed, otherwise the presentation lacks spiritual significance. Wordsworth, in his *Letter to a Friend of Robert Burns*, speaking of the biography of the poet, says:

"So much for facts and actions; and to what purpose relate them, even were they true, if the narrative cannot be heard without extreme pain; unless they are placed in such a light, and brought forward in such order, that they shall explain their own laws, and leave the reader in as little uncertainty as the mysteries of our nature will allow, respecting the spirit from which they derived their existence, and which governed the agent."

And he quotes from Burns himself the lines:

> "One point must still be greatly dark,
> The moving *why* they do it."

It is in the illuminating of this "greatly dark" point which should be the object of the dramatist's endeavor in his treatment of character. For, without attempting psychological subtleties, we may say that a man's life has two phases: its outer manifestation in deeds, and its inner in thoughts and feelings. The two phases are vitally connected, and the outer is not explicable save through the inner. Now, the bridge, the middle ground, between inner and outer, is found in words and in gestures. Gesture is not available to the dramatist except through the meagre medium of stage directions, and he must here trust to his actor, or, if the drama be read, to the imagination of his reader. Words, then, are his to use, and in words and acts he finds his material.

Self-expression through acts is the dramatist's special province, it is the bone and sinew of his work, which is thereby distinguished from the epic. But no one is fully represented by his deeds alone; even in the man who is freest there will be a reserve of tendencies that are never realized, impulses that, so far as outer activity is concerned, nullify each other. These the dramatist must consider, or his work will deteriorate into chronicle: —

> "Not on the vulgar mass
> Called 'work,' must sentence pass,
> Things done, that took the eye and had the price;
> O'er which, from level stand,
> The low world laid its hand,
> Found straightway to its mind, could value in a trice;
>
> "But all, the world's coarse thumb
> And finger failed to plumb,
> So passed in making up the main account;
> All instincts immature,
> All purposes unsure,
> That weighed not as his work, yet swelled the man's
>   amount.
>
> "Thoughts hardly to be packed
> Into a narrow act,
> Fancies that broke through language and escaped;
> All I could never be,
> All, men ignored in me,
> This, I was worth to God, whose wheel the pitcher
>   shaped."

We have seen what this fundamental principle usually involves as to the hero's position and culture. In the technique of the drama it also has certain corollaries. Two dramatic expedients have here their source, namely, the soliloquy and the confidant. Each is employed to meet a real need, and each is to some extent legitimate. The soliloquy, with its subspecies, the stage "aside," is, it is true, usually unnatural, but it is not therefore to be wholly condemned. It is the conventional way of letting us know the inner state of the actor, which we cannot otherwise be made to understand. This is the purpose of the first soliloquy of Richard III, of the soliloquies of Macbeth and of Hamlet, of the exquisite orchard scene in *Romeo and Juliet,* of the lyric outburst of Antigone before she is carried off by the guards.

The soliloquy has, indeed, been abused. Even Shakespeare does not always escape the Senecan faults of declamation and rhetoric for their own sake; but to counterbalance this we have the Hamlet reveries, and those two wonderfully effective variations of the species, the porter scene and the sleep-walking scene in *Macbeth.*

The other expedient, that of the confidential friend, to whom the actor may lay bare his inmost soul, is as old as the Greek drama. It came into modern drama, like so many other dramatic furnishings, through Seneca, the nurse or companion in his tragedies being transferred bodily to the French and the English stage, there to undergo many superficial, but no essential modifications.

Both these stage expedients, however, have been the butt of much derision, some of it just enough, and modern playwrights usually try to avoid recourse to them. Where this can be done without sacrificing clearness, it is a distinct gain. Ibsen scarcely uses them at all, and though his plays are sometimes obscure, it is not for this reason. In the second part of Wildenbruch's *Heinrich und Heinrich's Geschlecht*, however, the character of Prince Heinrich suffers, being in the highest degree subtle, complex, apparently contradictory, while we are given no key to its solution. On the other hand, it is instructive to note how, in *Strafford*, Browning has succeeded in portraying with masterly completeness the hero's inner nature, with very little use of soliloquy in the ordinary sense of the term, and with no confidant — for Lady Carlisle cannot be rightly so called. He has done this by carefully arranging the succession of the scenes so that, as Strafford confronts in turn the king, the court, Lady Carlisle, Pym, and the rest, the shiftings in his attitude make clear to us without further commentary that complex inner life which each of his fellows knows only in part and estimates untruly. The play *Strafford* is here and there marred by the obscurity that is Browning's greatest fault, and that is due to a careless and incomplete expression of his thought, yet even as it stands it is worth close study as one of the most magnificent dramatic creations in our literature. Its motto might have been the lines from

Ben Ezra quoted above, for the author has taken
an historic pèrson, the record of whose acts has
seemed enigmatical if not despicable, and has
restored or created the soul behind the acts — a
soul whose sad grandeur is the more moving because its fate has been to walk before men in the
garb of meanness and treachery.

There are other ways of arousing sympathy
besides the direct expression by the actor of his
motives and feelings.   Often the simple portrayal
of other phases of his nature than those brought
out in the chief action will be the best possible
means to this end, and many side-scenes in the
great dramas are of this nature.   In *Julius Cæsar*
a comparison with the Plutarch version shows that
the chief additions made by the dramatist were of
this sort.   Such are the elaboration of the quarrel
scene, barely mentioned in Plutarch, the transfer-
ence to this scene of the announcement of Cal-
purnia's death, the exquisitely tender passage
where Brutus is with his guards and with the boy
Lucius.   Addressing Lucius, he says:

" What, thou speak'st drowsily?
    Poor knave, I blame thee not; thou art o'erwatch'd;"

then, to Varro and Claudius:

    "I pray you, sirs, lie in my tent and sleep;
    *   *   *   *   *   *   *

Var.   So please you, we will stand and watch your
pleasure.

Bru.   I will not have it so: lie down, good sirs;

    *   *   *   *   *   *   *

     Look, Lucius, here's the book I sought for so;
     I put it in the pocket of my gown.

Luc.   I was sure your lordship did not give it me.
Bru.   Bear with me, good boy, I am much forgetful."

These lines give us a glimpse of another phase
of his character, which we should never have seen
in the patriot who killed his friend because he
deemed him a tyrant.   And they make an appeal
to our love, while the patriot might have moved
only our admiration and respect.   Such appeals
seem to occur naturally in the great dramas, thus
we find one in *Lear*, IV, 7, the scene between
Lear and Cordelia, which is not needed for the
action.   Turning to the Greek drama, we may
instance the little scene between Œdipus and his
daughters, which, coming after the earlier scenes,
brings out a side of his nature that was needed to
counterbalance its harsher aspects.

"Nay, let *my* fate go whither it will: but as touching
my children, — I pray thee, Creon, take no care on thee for
my sons; they are men. . . .   But my two girls, poor hapless ones, — who never knew my table spread apart, or lacked
their father's presence, but ever in all things shared my
daily bread, — I pray thee, care for *them;* and — if thou
canst — suffer me to touch them with my hands, and to in-
dulge my grief.   Grant it, prince, grant it, thou noble heart!
Ah, could I but once touch them with my hands, I should
think that they were with me, even as when I had sight. . . .

[CREON's *Attendants lead in the children* ANTIGONE *and* ISMENE.]

Ha? O ye gods, can it be my loved ones that I hear sobbing, — can Creon have taken pity on me and sent me my children — my darlings? Am I right?" etc.[1]

In *Antigone*, too, the character of the heroine has throughout been sustained at a degree of tensity that is almost sternness, the other side must be brought out if our sympathies are to be touched; and the author's sure instinct meets the need in her last words, where she almost breaks down as her love of life and joy assert themselves. With this may be compared the closely similar scene in *The Cenci*, though here there is not quite the same need for it, since the little scenes between Beatrice and her mother, her little brother, and her lover have kept us conscious, throughout the play, of the tenderer, more lovable side of the girl's nature.

In *Hamlet* we would be tempted to call the scene with Ophelia (III, 1) another such; it certainly was given this value by Booth's rendering, but Shakespeare's own intention is not so certain. His purpose here, as elsewhere in the character, may have been a little blurred by the older tradition, and it is not safe to build too much on his treatment.[2]

In *Coriolanus* such touches are almost wholly lacking, and we miss them, for it is especially in

---

[1] *Œdipus Tyrannus*, trans. Jebb, pp. 263 ff.
[2] Cf. *supra.* p. 30 and note.

those characters whose tendency is toward sternness that the dramatist must be careful to evoke
sympathy.

To turn to a modern drama, this was one of the
problems that Wildenbruch had to face in treating
the subject of Emperor Heinrich. He had to
arouse us to keen sympathy with a man whose iron
will and harsh exterior seemed singularly unpropitious. His solution is unique and masterly.
He treats his main action in four acts, and in place
of the other act inserts a prologue wherein he
brings before us his hero as a boy of ten years,
emotional, sensitive, generous, headstrong, in the
first sense of the word, magnanimous. In the
swiftly moving, highly condensed and suggestive
scenes of this prologue we are made to feel the
limitless possibilities for good and evil in the
child's nature; we see, too, the kind of influences
with which he is surrounded — violence and evil
passion on the one hand, the coldness of a narrow
and conventional, if not a merely superficial, piety
on the other.

When the play proper opens, and we see the
little prince become a king, harsh, haughty, ruth-
less, insolent toward God and man, we are not
repelled, for we remember the royal nature of the
boy, and we feel what must have been the grinding
pain of the years that have turned his good to evil.
Every bitter word of the king is so calculated as
to remind us of the boy, and where the group
around him see only a harsh tyrant, brutally mock-

ing his conquered enemies and bitter even to his friends, we see in the very brutality and bitterness the perverted expression of a lovable nature.

No drama, then, can represent merely the acts of the persons concerned; it must represent these acts in the light of the actors' motives, their moods, their ideals. But the proportionate emphasis on what we have roughly called the inner and the outer varies greatly in the work of different dramatic writers, or even in the different dramas of the same writer. If we compare, with this in mind, the dramas of Shakespeare and of Browning, we see that in general Browning emphasizes the inner life, Shakespeare the outer. Shakespeare sees his characters primarily as acting men among men; but because he sees them truly, not superficially, he sees also the man behind the activity, and, though valuing the outer, does not ignore the inner life. Browning proceeds conversely. Following Ben Ezra's creed, he sees his characters as souls whose outer activity only partly represents them, and he fixes our attention, primarily, upon their inner activity. Shakespeare's emphasis is on the act first, and then on the spiritual state causing it or resulting from it; Browning's is on the spiritual state first, and only secondarily on the act into which it passes, or from which it arises. Shakespeare's treatment is, apparently, though not really, external: he prefers to set before us, in the vividest manner possible, the outer activity of the person, and let us from that

K

infer the inner state.   Thus Macbeth merely refers in passing to "these dreams that shake us nightly," and of Lady Macbeth's spiritual experience we get scarcely a glimpse until the fifth act.   Again, what Coriolanus undergoes we only guess at through stray hints and by inference from his deeds and the situations in which he is placed.   We know that a soldier and a patriot does not go over to the enemy without war of spirit; we know that when a man whose pride has been unyielding gives way to his mother's prayers and reverses his action, it means an inner upheaval; we know that when he finds the enemy he has befriended turning again and rending him, the experience is bitter; but in each of these cases our knowledge is chiefly inferential.

Compare with this Browning's treatment of what might have been a similar theme.   We say "might have been," because in *Luria* as actually treated, the similarity of its original story to that of Coriolanus is scarcely recognizable.   The story in its bare outlines is this: A young Moor, with a genius for warfare, comes to Florence and devotes his talents to her service.   He is given the command in the war against Pisa, and conducts affairs to the point where victory is certain and there is needed only the mechanical carrying out of his plans. The Florentine leaders, however, mistrust Luria's single-mindedness, and fear that after the victory he will use his army to make himself master of the city.   To prevent this, they enter against him accusations of treachery, and arrange for his secret trial and execution. The Pisan general, Tiburzio, chancing upon evidence of their double dealing, discloses it to Luria, and invites him to come over to the Pisans. Luria refuses, completes the orders for the final battle, then takes poison. As he is dying, the Florentine representatives seek him, having by Tiburzio's testimony been convinced of the injustice of their suspicions. But Luria dies.

The likeness and the contrast in the two stories of Luria and Coriolanus need not be pointed out. For the present purpose what is interesting is the difference in method of treatment. First, the crowds and the large groups of men found in *Coriolanus* disappear, and instead we have a little group of seven persons, whose central figure, Luria, is brought and kept under the full blaze of light. Every thought, every feeling, every impulse is revealed from its birth to its fruition. And not this one figure alone, but the others as they come near him, as their activity affects him, are illumined; their motives, too, are searched, till one comes to feel that, after all, the act is nothing compared to the spiritual life behind the act.

But it is not the dramatist's part to feel this; what he should feel is that the act is everything, when understood in the light of the spiritual life behind the act, and Browning's strength becomes his weakness, his seer's vision of the spiritual man makes him lose grip on those outer activities of

life which are indispensable parts of the dramatist's material.   Such phrases as

> "Thoughts hardly to be packed
> Into a narrow act,"

or,

> " the vulgar mass called ' work ' "

are significant of the tendency which sometimes
mars his poetic work and lends a color of justice
to the remark lately made, "Browning's plays are
great poems — and they really ought to be drama-
tized."

In *Strafford* and *A Blot in the 'Scutcheon*, however, the balance of emphasis is kept within the
bounds of great dramatic art; in *Luria*, *Colombe's
Birthday*, *A Soul's Tragedy*, it is, in varying degree, less perfect; while in *Sordello* and *Paracel-
sus*, where the inner quite overbalances the outer,
the poet has judiciously abandoned the strictly
dramatic form.

The extreme of this tendency to portray the
inner life at the expense of the outer is seen in
the so-called dramas of Mæterlinck.   The author
boldly declares that his business is not with acts
at all, but with the spiritual life which even words
are almost powerless to reveal.   His theory, like
his work, shows a curious lack of the sense of
proportion, and his dramas, where they are great,
confute his theory.

Shakespeare, however, though his treatment
reverses Browning's emphasis, is not always the

same. Between the balance of inner and outer activity in *Coriolanus* and that in *Macbeth* there is almost as much difference as between Shakespeare's general method and Browning's. There is certainly more difference than there is between *Macbeth* and *A Blot in the 'Scutcheon*. *Coriolanus* is the most external of the great tragedies, *Macbeth* the most consistently spiritual, though *Hamlet*, in parts, goes further than anything else of Shakespeare's.

This brings us to another question — the question of so-called character-development. It has been maintained that much character-development is to be found in Shakespeare, and ten Brink, for example, finds in *Romeo and Juliet* a great change in Juliet between the Capulet's ball and the Capulet's tomb. A change, certainly; but the question is, what is the nature of the change? is it true development of character or merely different manifestations of the same character?

Evidently there is need for defining of terms. A person may be regarded as a complex of many qualities, whose absolute intensities and relative proportions determine the person's "character." By the use and disuse of these qualities in daily life, these absolute intensities may be increased or diminished, and their relative proportions thereby permanently altered. This constitutes character-development as we ordinarily use the term in real life. In this sense, Tito, in George Eliot's *Romola*, exemplifies character-development, and

Romola herself does so to a less extent. In *Middlemarch*, Lydgate, Rosamond, Dorothea, all show it; in *The Mill on the Floss*, Maggie Tulliver shows it; in *Daniel Deronda*, Gwendolen Harleth shows it.

In this same sense, we certainly get character-development in *Macbeth*. He himself recognizes this, when he says:

> "I have almost forgot the taste of fears:
> The time has been, my senses would have cool'd
> To hear a night-shriek; and my fell of hair
> Would at a dismal treatise rouse and stir
> As life were in't: I have supped full with horrors;
> Direness, familiar to my slaughterous thoughts,
> Cannot once start me." [1]

But it is a mistake to take this single play as typical of Shakespeare's work. In this respect, as in others, it is exceptional, and the change in character shown in its hero is different in kind from that shown in *Othello* or in *Coriolanus* or in *Julius Cæsar*. In *Othello*, indeed, the difference between the well-poised, confident general who faces the Venetian council, and the frenzied, half-savage man of the final scene,— the difference here is apparently greater than between the Macbeth of Act I and of Act V, but the source of the difference is not the same, and its significance is not the same. In *Othello* we see the gradual arousing of a passionate nature until it reaches a white heat that destroys itself and those nearest it; but this

[1] *Macbeth*, V, 5.

is not character-development, it is the temporary calling into play of one particular set of passions already mature in the character, though at first inactive because not aroused. It is, of course, by the arousing of passions, by the giving of them free play, that they grow, and in this sense the action of Othello must be regarded as forming one link in the development of all the persons concerned. If Othello had lived, he could not afterward have been quite the same man he was before, but this is not the aspect of the action that is emphasized in the play.

With the exception of *Macbeth*, *Lear*, and possibly *Hamlet*, Shakespeare's plays do not show development in this sense. What they do show is the blazing up of powers and passions out of quiescence into activity, and if we call this development it is merely because every act that a person performs and every outbreak of passion may be said to be one link in the causal chain determining as well as indicating character.

If we turn to Browning, we find the case slightly different. *A Soul's Tragedy* certainly shows character-development; not only shows it, but bases thereon the significance of the "tragedy." Ibsen's *A Doll's House* shows it; for, though the changes begin and culminate very rapidly, they are real and permanent, not merely the evincing of hitherto latent characteristics. Here, as in *A Soul's Tragedy*, the focus of attention is upon these permanent changes, only that, whereas in Browning the soul is lost, in Ibsen (from his standpoint at least) the soul finds itself and sets out to save itself.   The same is true of *Colombe's Birthday*. Note, however, that in the case of Nora and of Colombe the limits of the dramatic form make possible only a suggestion of the development, and each play ends with an outlook into a future that we know will bring further changes along the lines of those already begun.

It is perhaps true that the drama can scarcely do more than thus suggest development, and Shakespeare may have been right in not attempting more.   The life-history of Tito Melema or of Maggie Tulliver could not, in the five acts of a drama, have been treated effectively, and such themes may better be left to be handled in the less restricted literary form of the novel.   What the drama primarily presents, is the critical moment of conflict, with the spiritual changes therein involved.   It is this inner crisis, as worked out in the outer clash, the outer crisis as resulting from and reacting on the inner life, that it is the dramatist's function to portray.

CHAPTER V

PLOT IN COMEDY

IN many respects the laws of structure determined for the serious drama are equally valid for comedy, but there are also important differences between the two kinds of dramatic creation. First, it may be generally stated that in comedies the action of the plot is much more independent of the characters than it is in the serious drama: it is, as we have already implied, even possible to create a comic plot which shall be really comic, while its persons are nothing more than puppets, the development of the plot being wholly extraneous to the characters. This is the case in *The Comedy of Errors*, in much so-called farce, in much of the Spanish comedy. Again, the comic action is far less bound to emphasize law in its treatment of events; it can make free use of what we call accident and chance.

Passing now to a more detailed consideration of its structure, we find that comedies fall into two main groups, according as their comic interest does or does not determine the main plot. Compare, for example, *King Henry IV* with *Every Man in His Humour*. In the former there is a serious main plot, based on events in English history wherein the fiercest passions were aroused and the largest interests involved, and wherein the actors were of heroic type.   The comic interest is found in a number of interspersed scenes whose action is loosely connected with the serious main plot; cut out these scenes, and with few changes the play becomes a serious historical drama.   In Jonson's play, on the other hand, the exact converse is the case.   The serious interest — and there is very little — is subordinate.   The comic interest is not merely developed in the main plot, it actually constitutes it; cut out this and you destroy the play.

These two plays may be accepted as typical of two great classes of comedies.   To those of the first type the name "romantic comedy" has been given, for reasons not wholly connected with its structure; those of the second type have been variously styled, according to considerations foreign to this discussion.   To it belong all of Aristophanes, most of Plautus and Terence, most of Jonson and Molière, the comedies of Massinger and Middleton and Congreve.   With *Henry IV* are to be classed all of Shakespeare's comedies except *Love's Labour's Lost*, *The Comedy of Errors*, *The Merry Wives of Windsor*, *The Taming of the Shrew*.

Since the romantic comedy has as its basis a serious main plot, and its comic interests are episodic, it may be temporarily disregarded.   It is in the second class of comedies that we shall find the typical comic structure.

Reverting to our illustration of the primitive form of comic plot,— our case of the man who sits down on the floor,— let us start again from this. In actual life we know that this may occur for various reasons: (1) he may have miscalculated the position of the chair, and the fault is therefore his own; or (2) the chair may break, and the fault is no one's; or (3) some one with malice prepense may have pulled the chair from under him, or may have placed a weak chair where he was likely to sit.

So in comedies. The action may be one where the mistakes, the comic disappointments, arise out of the weakness of the victim, and he alone is to blame, or they may spring from circumstance, and no one is responsible, or they may be deliberately planned by one of the play's persons, an arch-intriguer, assisted, perhaps, by lucky accident, which he knows how to turn to account.

An example of the first sort is seen, though not with perfect clearness, in *Love's Labour's Lost*, through the fourth act. The four gentlemen have simply miscalculated their own powers and attempted something beyond them. Hence, all fail signally, and the great scene for which the play is planned, IV, 3, merely presents this failure. Each does in turn expose his fellow, in true "house-that-Jack-built fashion," but no one of them has planned the downfall of another.

The second kind is exemplified with typical

clearness in *The Comedy of Errors*. Here the whole complication is the result of chance, no one guides its progress, and its conclusion is as much accident as any part of its course.

The third sort is seen, as has just been said, in the last act of *Love's Labour's Lost*, but it is better to select an instance where the entire play is constructed on this principle. Among the multitude of such, we may mention, as being, for one reason or another, unusually good instances, Jonson's *Every Man in His Humour* (Brainworm and Ed. Knowell are the intriguers); *The Silent Woman* (arch-intriguers, Dauphine, Clerimont, and Lovewit); Chapman's *All Fools* (intriguers, Rinaldo, for the main plot, Cornelio, for a subordinate counter-plot); Massinger's *A New Way to Pay Old Debts* (intriguers, Wellborn, for the main plot, Allworth and Lovell for the underplot); Molière's *L'École des Maris* (intriguers, Isabelle and Valère). Among them, the simplest in structure is Molière's, and next comes Massinger's, which we will take as a type because it is English. The argument is, briefly, as follows:

Act I. Wellborn, a prodigal, has ruined himself by his excesses, and his estate has passed into the hands of his uncle, Overreach, an unscrupulous old man who has amassed large wealth by sharp practice. In despair, Wellborn turns for help to Lady Allworth, a rich widow whose late husband he had once befriended in time of need. Out of

gratitude for this, Lady Allworth consents to feign
a betrothal to Wellborn.

ACTS II, III, and IV.   On the strength of his
expectations, Wellborn is instantly restored to
credit.   His uncle is anxious to facilitate the
match, hoping ultimately to get hold of Lady Allworth's wealth as he already has got Wellborn's.
He therefore pays his nephew's debts and enter-
tains him royally.

Overreach has a daughter, Margaret, whom he
longs to see married to a title, and he offers her
in marriage to Lord Lovell.   In the lord's service
is young Allworth, stepson to Lady Allworth, who
loves Margaret and is loved by her.   Lord Lovell
befriends his cause, and while feigning consent to
the marriage for himself, helps young Allworth
convey Margaret away and marry her.

Meanwhile Marrall, an attorney and an unscrupulous attaché of Overreach, decides that it will
be more profitable to serve Wellborn.

ACT V.   Through Marrall's agency it is discovered that the deed transferring Wellborn's
estates to his uncle is worthless, and the owner-
ship, therefore, reverts to Wellborn.   Next, Overreach learns of the marriage of his daughter with
young Allworth.   At the double catastrophe he
goes mad.

Now, it will be seen that the entire structure of
the plot depends on the deliberately planned
schemes of Wellborn and Allworth to outwit Over-

reach. Does this differ from the plan of the serious drama?

In a sense, we might adopt the phraseology of the tragedy, and call the action "a losing struggle, by an imperfect character, against the overpowering forces of life." We might say that there is found here, the three things essential to tragedy: suffering, struggle, causality.

In a sense, yes; but in a sense so different from the tragic that, though the words may be unchanged, the ideas can no longer be treated as the same.

First: the character is indeed imperfect, but the imperfections are here regarded as material for comic contrast, and subjects for judicial reprehension, not for pity and sympathy. This has already been discussed.

Next, as to the struggle. The result of it in both cases is the overthrow of some one, but the process is different in principle and significance — as different as is our case where the malicious person pulls away the chair from the case where two men grapple in a fair fight. In the serious drama, the hero is contending, it may be against one man, it may be against a host, it may be against himself, it may be against the remorseless "course of things." We may even know from the beginning that the struggle must end in failure, as we do know in the *Œdipus*, or in *The Cenci;* but our hero really fights, he has his chance, all his energies go into the struggle and are staked on the issue. In this kind of comedy, on the other hand, he does not really fight: he is a victim, his overthrow is not really inevitable, it is artfully prearranged.

Finally, the causality in the two kinds of drama is totally different. Tragedy must be based on law, and, as we saw, it is better for the tragedian not to use such events as have about them an air of chance. For comedy this requirement is not imperative. The main thing is the presentation of striking incongruities, and we do not care whether these are evidently grounded in the law of the universe or not; in fact, the range of comic view being limited, it is often better that it should not call too vividly to mind the iron rule of law. Accordingly, we find in comedy the widest license allowed. When Shakespeare, borrowing for his use the old story of the twin brothers, complicates its situations by postulating a second pair of twins as servants to these brothers, we do not cavil at the improbability. If he chose to postulate two pairs of twin sisters, too, we should not object, provided he was master of his material. These considerations have, as will appear, an important bearing on the nature of the comic catastrophe.

So much for general questions. Contrast now more particularly the plans of the two types of drama:

The serious drama usually begins in an apparent equilibrium, from which the conflict develops. In the first part of the play, one of the two contending forces is paramount; in the second, the other, and the outcome is a final equilibrium wholly different from the apparent equilibrium at the beginning.

In the comedy just summarized the case is quite different. Instead of an aggressor meeting an aggressor, there is an aggressor and a victim. It is the natural result of the difference in principle between comedy and tragedy. Instead of a conflict of forces, the comic plots of this type present a process rather like the picking of the lock of a safe; it may be interesting, it may involve great ingenuity and address, but it is on a wholly different basis.

To pursue, for a moment, the figure of the lock: — the beginning of the play presents the problem; we see the strong safe, with its lock, apparently secure; we see the would-be lock-breaker, his eyes fixed on the safe, his fingers twitching to get at its secrets. Next, it is hinted that despite this seeming security there are weak points — possibly the lock can be forced. Then comes the process of forcing it, until finally the successful lock-breaker carries out his scheme and enjoys the fruits of his ingenuity.

What the corollaries, are which may be deduced from the fundamental difference between the two problems, will be evident if we consider, one by one, the logical divisions of this type of drama.

[1] *Exposition.* This has no peculiar features. In the Massinger play, the first act is mainly ex-

positional, the rising action being only suggested at the end of the third scene.

[2] *Exciting Force and Rising Action.* The exciting force is always found in the resolution of the arch-intriguer to outwit his victim. In the play before us, it is Wellborn's desperate resolve to have one more try at fortune. Sometimes, as often in the plays of Plautus and Terence, a preliminary action is presented, which is the immediate occasion of this resolution, *e.g.* a young man falls in love, and plans how to circumvent his father, who opposes him. It is evident that, if in such a case the love-plot is given serious enough emphasis, and our attention is drawn to the issues therein involved, and away from the circumventing of the authorities considered in itself, the play may become serious instead of comic. The emphasis is laid, not on the intellectual problem, but on the emotional crisis. This comes near being the case in *As You Like It;* it is the case in *Romeo and Juliet,* and perhaps the impression of weakness left upon us by the last act of this play is partly due to this resemblance between its plan and that of the ordinary comedy; for its tragic catastrophe is brought about, not by the essential constitution of things and the nature of the spiritual problem in itself, but by the accidental failure of an ingeniously arranged scheme which might just as well have been successful.

[3] *Climax*, and [4] *Falling Action.* There is, strictly speaking, no climax and no falling action.

L

For, from the very nature of the case, the victim cannot retaliate; it would spoil the play if he did. The movement of the rising action goes steadily forward through the play, though not necessarily at uniform rate. From the standpoint of the intriguer, it might be represented by a line trending upward; from the standpoint of the victim, by one trending downward. In the Massinger play, there is no climax, in the sense in which we have hitherto been using the term. The only possibility of making one would be to take it as formed by Act III, Scene 2, because this scene is the most elaborate one in the play, and the only one in which both main plot and subplot are interwoven. But such an external test is not the sort one uses for tragedy.

[5] *Catastrophe.* It presents the completed results of the intriguer's plans, and the total overthrow of the victim. In contrast to the tragic catastrophe it need not be causally determined by what has preceded. Here, as elsewhere throughout the action, causality is not emphasized, and here as elsewhere chance may determine the issue. Thus, in the play mentioned, one-half of the misfortune of Overreach is due, not to Wellborn's machinations at all, save very indirectly, but to the "Deus ex machina" in the person of Marrall. Nor need the catastrophe have any quality of finality; it is sufficient that it furnish some sort of finish, which may not preclude further activity, renewed machinations, more victimizing, or even

a later "turning of the worm" in a retaliatory stroke. Whereas tragedy must be final, comedy need not be more than provisional; it offers a solution only of the specific problem presented. Not that its conclusion is bound to be provisional; this will depend partly upon what has been the underlying purpose of the intrigue. Compare, as illustrating this, the character of the conclusion in *A New Way to Pay Old Debts*, which is approximately final, with that of *The Alchemist*, which impresses one as not more than provisional. In many cases, it is true, an air of conclusiveness is given by a sweeping moral regeneration of all knaves, taking place in the last act, but this is usually specious and unsatisfying; it is always quite different from the fundamental and absolute readjustment in the true tragic solution.

These are the chief differences to be noted between the comic and the tragic plot. Subordinate differences will, of course, follow as corollaries, but to take them up here would involve detailed analysis of comedy after comedy. The essential thing is to have marked the principal lines of divergence in the two types.

There are, indeed, cases where the lines seem to cross, and perhaps really do so. In *Othello*, for example, we have an action which conforms, in some respects, rather to the comic than the tragic type. Othello himself is less a fighter than a victim, while Iago's attitude from the beginning is that of the arch-intriguer in the comedies we have been discussing. He considers himself injured, as does Wellborn; he plans a deliberate attack, as does Wellborn, and enlists the help of others; he chooses the point where his victim is weakest and makes his assault there, appealing to Othello's impulsive and unreasoning love, as Wellborn appeals to his uncle's consuming greed of gain. There is, moreover, in Iago's attitude a kind of grim, colossal humor, while in his scheming there is a cool, if somewhat crude, power that makes us respect him and wins our intellectual sympathy, as does the arch-intriguer in a comedy. The divergence from comedy is found in the fact that (1) the character of the victim is so noble, and is so treated as to evoke our emotional sympathy; and (2) that he is strong enough, when finally aroused, to retaliate with terrible energy and with such terrible effectiveness that our thought is drawn away from the intellectual phases of the case to its emotional issues.[1] But, great as these differences are, the similarity in plan of the first four acts can scarcely be ignored, and it may be one reason why the play does not appeal to all of us as being tragic in the highest sense.

To take an instance of the converse: Molière's *Le Misanthrope* seems, to some readers at least, not at all the typical comedy, and if we examine

---

[1] Compare the case of Shylock, in *The Merchant of Venice*, where the feeling toward the victim may range, according to the character of the audience and of the actor, all the way from pity to scornful derision.

the plan of the plot we shall find that it has traits distinctive rather of tragedy than of comedy; it presents, namely, a real conflict of forces, and one that is grounded in the spiritual nature of the persons concerned. With very slight changes it might have been made a tragedy, and as it is, when read in some moods, it is apt to seem more tragic than comic.

To resume: the plan of the comic action differs decidedly from that of the serious drama in the character of its conflict, in its freedom from the necessity of emphasizing law and its consequent license in use of chance or accident, in the absence of a true climax and a true falling action, and in the nature of its catastrophe. If the serious drama is represented by the projected pyramid, the comedy, such as Massinger's, may be represented by two lines, an ascending one for the intriguer, a descending one for the victim.

Applying these results to other comedies, it will be seen that they conform fairly well. In the comedies of Plautus the victim is usually a rich old man, the intriguer usually his son or nephew, always assisted by a slave, and often by some other young man. The differences between play and play are found in the differences in the method of attack and in the motives for it. In Jonson's comedies the plan is the same in principle, but the schemes are exceedingly complicated; there are usually several intriguers with plans somewhat opposed, and there results a number of separate little puzzles, with separate solutions, but all finally brought together in the general solution of the dénouement. Molière's plots, again, are more simple.[1]

Turning now from this large group of comedies, let us see how far its principles apply to the group loosely classed as "romantic." At the beginning of the chapter we turned away from these because the other, by virtue of its simplicity and its clearness of definition, lent itself more readily to analysis. The results thus gained may help us in dealing with the more difficult and elusive "romantic" comedy, or, at least, may afford a firm base from which we may proceed to its investigation.

In the intrigue comedy it was noted that, in supplying the intriguer with a motive for his scheming, the love-interest was usually employed, and it was suggested that if the love-interest was sufficiently emphasized it might overbalance the comic interest, and the play might become more or less serious. In turning from the plays of Plautus to those of Terence one notices, in some cases, a tendency toward this very thing. Terence's more delicate talent seems to have inclined him to lay a slightly greater emphasis on the serious element of the plot, and there results a change in the proportionate values of the serious and the comic elements. It varies in different plays, but

[1] For a fuller discussion of this type of comedy, *cf.* Woodbridge, *Studies in Jonson's Comedy*.

on the whole it seems fair to say that Terence treats the motive-interest, if we may so distinguish it from the intrigue-interest, with a tenderness of touch and gentle delicacy of sympathy that in a later age would have developed into the so-called "romantic" plot. In the *Heautontimorumenos*, the remorseful old father doing self-imposed penance for his harshness toward his son, the devotion of that son to his mistress, Antiphila, the little touches that sketch the character of the girl Antiphila herself; in the *Andria*, the overwhelming love of Pamphilus and Glycerium, which seems to have in it something more than the passion we find depicted in Plautus; — these give us glimpses, though no more than glimpses, of a possible development into another sort of comedy.

Such a development is found in full maturity in the work of Shakespeare; and though we may not take the plays of Terence as a link in an actual evolutionary chain, — for the evolution took place on other lines, — we may use them in our own thought as furnishing a transition phase between the two kinds of comedy.[1]

In dealing with Shakespeare we have, it must be remembered, only approximate dates, and cannot base too much on chronology, yet enough seems established to give us some rough notions of grouping and development. The comedies, fol-

---

[1] In Italian comedy, however, there seems actually to have been some such evolution. *Cf.* Violet Paget's *Studies of the Eighteenth Century in Italy*.

lowing the approximate chronology now agreed upon, may be arranged as follows:

> Love's Labour's Lost.
> The Comedy of Errors.
> The Two Gentlemen of Verona.
> A Midsummer Night's Dream.

> The Merchant of Venice.
> The Taming of the Shrew.
> King Henry IV, two parts.
> The Merry Wives of Windsor.
> Much Ado about Nothing.
> As You Like It.
> Twelfth Night.

> All's Well that Ends Well.
> Measure for Measure.

> Cymbeline.
> The Winter's Tale.
> The Tempest.

Of the earliest group two, *Love's Labour's Lost* and *The Comedy of Errors*, have been already accounted for. In both the comic interest determines the main plot, which is in the one case developed out of the characters, in the other out of pure incident apart from character. Yet in the latter case it is significant that Shakespeare, using Plautus' plot, added to it here and there touches of seriousness not in his original, and the proportions of the two elements in the play are more nearly as in some of Terence's comedies.

In *The Two Gentlemen of Verona* we have the romantic comedy proper: there is the comic episode, which could be cut out without maiming the play's structure, and the serious love-plot, double (as often in Terence) and following in its logical divisions the lines of the serious drama. Because it is so simple and typical, it is worth while to examine it somewhat in detail.

ACT I. *Exposition:* love of Proteus and Julia, friendship of Proteus and Valentine.

Rising Action: Valentine leaves for Milan, Proteus also is to be sent thither.

ACT II. *Exposition, continued:* love of Valentine and Silvia.

Rising Action, continued: in development of Proteus' treachery toward Julia and toward Valentine. A possible opposition is hinted in Julia's resolution to go to seek Proteus.

ACT III. *Climax:* apparent success of Proteus' plans, and banishment of Valentine.

ACT IV. *Return Action:* turn of fortune for Valentine suggested in his being made king of the outlaws; for Proteus it is suggested by the appearance of Julia in Milan; for both it is precipitated by Silvia's plan to run away.

ACT V. *End of Return Action*, and *Resolution:* Silvia's flight accomplished, the pursuit of her brings about the solution.

Here it will be seen that there is a true conflict of forces, a true rise, turning-point, and descent.

And if Proteus has some of the characteristics of the arch-intriguer, it is the serious, not the comic aspect of his activity that is emphasized, and its criminal nature.

The broad comedy in the play is embodied in the episodes where Speed and Launce appear. They could be cut out, yet they are really related to the main-plot scenes. For, as the Greeks used to follow up their tragedies by a comic parody, so Shakespeare seems here to have intended a parody of his own serious situations. In II, 2, is presented the parting of the two lovers; in the next scene Launce appears and sets forth, with the help of his slippers and his cane, his own farewell to his family: the tears of his parents, the wails of his cat, and the unnatural indifference of his "stony-hearted dog." Again, in III, 1, immediately following upon Valentine's desperate grief at the separation from Silvia, comes Speed with the announcement that he, too, is in love, and he proceeds to discuss the situation. The parallelism may be accidental, but it can scarcely be deemed so. A similar case occurs in *Love's Labour's Lost*, in the Armado-Costard-Jaquenetta episodes, while in *As You Like It* the parody is elaborated, in Touchstone and Awdry, past the point of mere parody, almost into an independent sub-interest.

But, besides this burlesque treatment of the serious issue, there is, in the presentation of the issue itself, the beginning of a kind of comedy peculiar to Shakespeare, namely, a touching of the serious with a slightly comic light, — of the most tenderly delicate sort, it is true, but unmistakable comedy nevertheless. This is the case in the scenes in which Julia appears (note especially Act I, Scene 2). It is the first trace of the author's power to look at things in two ways at once, a first gleam of the genius that was later to look at the old Lear through the eyes of the "bitter fool," and utter his tragedy in a jest, "And yet I would not be thee, nuncle; thou hast pared thy wit o' both sides, and left nothing i' the middle ": (Goneril enters) "here comes one o' the parings."

In *A Midsummer Night's Dream*, again, there are the two distinct lines: one the love-interest, — double again, and as usual with the lines intercrossing until straightened out by Oberon, — and the other the comic interest in the tradesmen of Athens and their interlude. The third group, the fairies and Puck, brings in a semi-lyric element foreign to our present discussion. So far all is clear: the comic in the tradesmen's scenes is easily placed, and it does not affect the main plot. But once more, in this main plot, we find the note of comedy even stronger than in *The Two Gentlemen of Verona*, while in the entire treatment there is a tone of whimsicality that is perhaps a result of the midsummer night's witchery. The serious and the comic standpoints are represented for us in Oberon and Puck, as they look on at the confusion of the two pairs of lovers. Oberon, taking it earnestly, thinks of the consequences:

"What hast thou done? Thou hast mistaken quite
And laid the love-juice on some true-love's sight:
Of thy misprision must perforce ensue
Some true love turned and not a false turned true."

Puck, the mocker, enjoys the situation:

"Captain of our fairy band,
  Helena is here at hand;
And the youth, mistook by me,
  Pleading for a lover's fee.
Shall we their fond pageant see?
Lord, what fools these mortals be?
  Oberon.   Stand aside: the noise they make
Will cause Demetrius to awake.
  Puck.   Then will two at once woo one;
That must needs be sport alone;
And those things do best please me
That befall preposterously."

And again, when Oberon reprimands the imp:

"This is thy negligence: still thou mistakest.
Or else committ'st thy knaveries wilfully."

Puck answers, unabashed:

"Believe me, king of shadows, I mistook.

* * * * * * *

And so far am I glad it did so sort
As this their jangling I esteem a sport." [1]

And evidently the poet himself was able to see at
once with the eyes of Oberon and of Puck.

In *The Merchant of Venice* a sterner note is
struck. As always, there is the episodic comedy

---

[1] *A Midsummer Night's Dream*, III, 2.

and the love-plots, but there is also the Shylock-Bassanio interest. And here the query intrudes itself: did Shakespeare mean the Shylock plot to be comic or not? It has, indeed, even now a grim kind of comic effect, but we must suspect that the Elizabethan audience laughed where we do not. Possibly Shakespeare meant him to be comic, and without purposing to do so lapsed occasionally into a sympathetic treatment simply because he could not help doing this with any character that he handled long. This would account on the one hand for the hardness of tone in the Jessica plot, and on the other hand for the sympathetic insight in such passages as Shylock's magnificent outburst in answer to Salarino:

"*Salar.* Why, I am sure, if he forfeit, thou wilt not take his flesh: what's that good for?

Shy. To bait fish withal: if it will feed nothing else, it will feed my revenge. . . . I am a Jew. Hath not a Jew eyes? hath not a Jew hands. . . . If you prick us, do we not bleed? if you tickle us, do we not laugh? if you poison us, do we not die? and if you wrong us, shall we not revenge?" etc.[1]

According to this interpretation, we see in Shylock, despite such passages, our familiar comic victim, grown indeed more formidable, and requiring, not the justice but the injustice of the law courts to overcome him, but the comic victim nevertheless, whose downfall, as in typical comedy of intrigue, brings with it the happiness of the

[1] *The Merchant of Venice*, III, 1,

lovers. Shakespeare's mistake, then, was in making us sympathize too keenly with Shylock, though, as we have said, this may not have been the case for his own day.

This brings us to *Henry IV*, whose structure we have already settled. For, though the character of Falstaff really overshadows the entire play, it does not affect its structure, and the comic scenes are episodic.

In *The Merry Wives of Windsor* we have a unique case: the episodic comedy of the two preceding plays is, by a *tour de force*, made the main plot of this one, while a serious subplot is added. The victimizing is an end in itself, instead of being, as in the usual comic main plot, a means to some other end; and Falstaff, from a unique comic hero, has deteriorated into a commonplace comic butt. He has lost his peculiar wit, and — most impossible of all — he takes himself seriously, so that instead of laughing with him we are laughing at him. The character of the play bears out the tradition concerning its writing; it is evidently a piece of hack work, and though the hack work of genius cannot be ignored, the play may, in the present discussion, be set one side.

The next three comedies form a closely related group, which need here scarcely be considered apart. All have serious love-plots and all have comic by-play, that in *Twelfth Night* being curiously affiliated with the type found in Molière and Jonson, while in Rosalind we might, if we chose, see an arch-intriguer turned somewhat ethereal and exceeding moral, managing the others for their best good and her own innocent amusement. In all three the serious plot is occasionally given a comic tone, the comedy being also partly perceived even by the participants themselves. In these three plays we get the perfection of the Shake-spearean comedy, and we need not go on to the last two groups, for, though the bitter jests of *All's Well that Ends Well* and *Measure for Measure* and the idyllic temperateness of *The Tempest* show a tre-mendous range in tone and many interesting points of detail, there is nothing new in underly-ing structure.

Pausing here, then, and looking over the range of Shakespearean comedy, we find certain qualities characterizing it: a main plot embodying the love-interest, and episodic scenes embodying the comic interest, the love-interest tinged with comedy yet not so as to destroy its seriousness. It is thus allied with both kinds of drama: with the serious, in that its main ends are serious and its use of the emotions is so; with the comic by reason of this touch of comedy in the treatment, and also by its emancipation from law. For these serious plots have in this respect almost as much license as has pure comedy, and, whereas tragedy is grounded in the spiritual laws of human life, these present to us situations constructed by the fancy and imagina-tion from materials furnished by human life. In the reconstruction, certain things are left out, and that which is above all emphasized in tragedy is here steadily ignored, the binding force of the law, — " Whatsoever a man soweth, that shall he also reap." The imagination is free to work, and in the result there is an element of the fanciful, even of the whimsical.

Thus, of the three forms, tragedy, comedy, and this Shakespearean type of comedy, each selects out of life certain parts — no one is complete. Comedy is, in one way, the most limited in its view and the most superficial, it emphasizes certain intellectual phases of things but leaves out others, and it avoids an appeal to the emotions; tragedy is the deepest, laying stress on the emotional phases of life, but treating them not simply in themselves, as does the lyric, but in their relations to will and to outer fact. The romantic comedy is somewhere between these two extremes : its treatment hovers between the surface view, which is characteristic of the comic, and the deeper insight that is essential to the tragic; it makes use of the emotions, but ignores their causal relations.

It will be evident that this intermediate position gives the fullest possible scope to the poetic imagination, and we see how in *The Tempest* and *A Midsummer Night's Dream* it almost passes out of drama proper and verges on what we might call free dramatic fantasia. It is because of these qualities, too, that it is to the lover of the drama peculiarly satisfying. It has neither the thinness that often characterizes pure comedy by reason of its preponderating intellectuality, nor the almost oppressive emotional intensity of tragedy; yet it is free to employ the resources of both tragedy and comedy, while it may range in tone from the temperateness of the epic to the emotional depth of the lyric. It has at once richness and delicacy; it is at once philosophical and fanciful; it is the most "poetic" of forms. Even Jonson, the high priest of the intellectual in drama, when, for the only time in his dramatic career, he gave freer play to the other side of his nature, adopted a form akin to this; and Shakespeare, though his mightiest achievements are in tragedy, attained in this form his most nearly perfect artistic excellence.

M

CHAPTER VI

CHARACTER-TREATMENT IN COMEDY

WE have already seen that, since the comic in character is based on imperfection, it is possible to regard this imperfection either with simple appreciation of its comic flavor, or judicially, or sympathetically.

As an example of the purely appreciative treatment, take the nurse in *Romeo and Juliet*. Here there is no tendency either toward the sympathy that verges on pity, or toward the judicial attitude that verges on satire. The character is presented without comment, and left for us to enjoy or overlook. There is no attempt to make her see her own weaknesses or suffer for them; there is not even any sign that the other persons in the play consider her comic. She is, as it were, taken for granted, as one of the comic things in a serious, if not a tragic, world. Be it noted that this absolutely non-committal presentation of a comic character is rather rare, even in Shakespeare, — still rarer outside his works. It is found in Molière and momentarily in Congreve, but each of these writers quickly relapses into the judicial attitude.

One remove away from this non-committal

manner of presentation toward the judicial type
is the character-treatment in *Love's Labour's Lost.*
The comic theme is found in the contrast between
vows and performance, between pretence and
reality.   It is treated in three ways.   First, in
Costard, we have the natural man, not aspiring,
indeed, but honest; his relations with Jaquenetta
are entirely naïve.   In contrast with him, Armado
is presented, who enforces with great parade of
superiority the sentence pronounced upon Costard,
and the next moment proceeds to outdo Costard
in transgression.   Note, however, that the author
lets him go without exposure, content with the
simple exhibition of his character.   Finally, there
are the four forsworn gentlemen.   The contrast
between their vow and their performance is first
developed, as in Armado's case; but when each
attempts to play the part of righteous censor of
his fellow, he is caught, and his hypocrisy is ex-
posed.   This is the first moral check.   The second
comes in the last act, where the ladies' practical
joke accentuates the lesson, and there results in
the case of Biron a veritable "reformed character,"
making his recantation:

> " Oh, never will I trust to speeches penn'd,
>   Nor to the motion of a schoolboy's tongue,
>   Nor never come in vizard to my friend,
>   Nor woo in rhyme, like a blind harper's song!
>   Taffeta phrases, silken terms precise,
>   Three-piled hyperboles, spruce affectation,
>
> *   *   *   *   *   *   *

I do forswear them; and I here protest,

*   *   *   *   *   *   *

Henceforth my wooing mind shall be express'd
In russet yeas and honest kersey noes." [1]

From the gentle irony of this play the transition
is clear, though the step is a long one, to Jonson's
satiric treatment of human infirmity.   Jonson, in
theory at least, was before all else the moralist,
conscious of his calling.   Comedy was to him a
means, not an end, and he never wearied of re-
peating his creed:

"The ends of all, who for the stage do write,
Are, or should be, to profit and delight." [2]

The "profit" is to be gained from the exposure of
folly and villany, the "delight," presumably, from
our perception of the masterly way in which the
playwright accomplishes his task, if not also from
the somewhat questionable pleasure of laughing at
the weaknesses of others.   Evidently with such
a theory it depends chiefly on the natural temper
of the writer and on the character of the society in
which he is thrown, whether his work will be pure
satire or satiric comedy.   Jonson's temper had in
it a touch of bitterness from which Molière's is
free, and there is a corresponding difference in the
work of the two writers.   Both deal with folly;
both have the consciousness of superiority to folly,
which is by no means inconsistent with true nobility of soul; but the Frenchman had always a

[1] *Love's Labour's Lost,* V, 2.
[2] *The Silent Woman,* Prologue.

philosophic sweetness of spirit that the Englishman seldom showed.

Yet in Jonson's work there are degrees. His first typical comedy, *Every Man in His Humour*, does, as its prologue promises,

" Sport with human follies, not with crimes,"

and though it distinctly bears the judicial stamp, the judgments are, for Jonson, gentle, and do not overbalance the flavor of comedy. In his next play, *Every Man Out of His Humour*, there is a marked increase in bitterness, while, to enforce his moral lessons, the writer creates a character (Asper in the induction, Macilente in the play) whose qualities are nearly Jonson's own, and through whose mouth the author makes his satiric comments on the persons of the play. In the two following comedies, *Cynthia's Revels* and *The Poetaster*, the office of author's spokesman is filled respectively by Crites for the first and by Horace for the second. In these two plays, moreover, the tone is yet more bitter — at times venomous — and the satire even degenerates, as satire is always in danger of doing, into personal attack by the author on his personal enemies. *Cynthia's Revels* is chiefly interesting because it shows almost all the faults that ever beset this type of comedy. Its treatment is labored and elaborate. It sets before us, on the one hand, a number of persons showing various kinds and degrees of folly and vice; on the other, a number of persons embody-

ing contrasting virtues; while, that the intent may
be perfectly clear, Crites is turned loose upon the
company to expose folly and convict the sinners
of their sin.   At the end comes their recantation,
curiously suggesting that of Biron quoted above:

"*Amorphus.*   From Spanish shrugs, French faces, smirks,
irpes, and all affected humors,
   Chorus.   Good Mercury defend us.
   Phantaste.   From secret friends, sweet servants, loves,
doves, and such fantastic humors,
   Chorus.   Good Mercury defend us," etc., etc.[1]

The taint of personal bitterness does not, however, mar all of Jonson's work.   In *Volpone* the
dramatic artist is plainly dominant, and the play
is an example of dramatic satire, perfect of its
kind, and possessed of a tone which is earnest
without being bitter, moral without being self-
righteous, and whose comic element takes the form
of grim irony that has in it something Titanic.
The play is to be classed less with comedy than
with what we may call satiric tragedy — such as
Jonson's *Sejanus* and *Catiline*, and Massinger's
The Roman Actor.

But the judicial attitude need not necessarily
be a moral one.   It may be mainly intellectual,
and one of Jonson's most brilliant productions,
The Alchemist, teaches nothing save, possibly, "Be
a knave if you like, but don't be a fool."   Almost
every person in the play is an arrant rogue, and the

---

[1] *Cynthia's Revels*, Palinode.

one honest man is outwitted and put to shame. It is a case of wit against wit, cunning against cunning, and the devil take the hindmost.

It has seemed advisable to treat Jonson thus at length, because he is generally acknowledged as the second English dramatist, while he is certainly the greatest English representative of the type of comedy we have been discussing. His work is, moreover, peculiarly interesting because it shows so many phases of the type and because, by illustrating the extreme as well as the more temperate forms, it shows what is the ultimate tendency of this kind of writing.

In Molière and Congreve the judicial type of comedy found a slightly different development. Both have the satiric note; but both are, though for different reasons, free from the bitterness of Jonson. Molière's exposure of the follies of the social man was done with a less heavy hand, and he smiled at life often where Jonson would have frowned, or where at least his smile would have been less sweet — more scornful. Molière dealt with somewhat the same types of men, but types reflecting the difference between the French court of Louis and the English society of the Stuarts, and bearing the stamp of a highly organized social order. His judgments are those, not of abstract morality, but of a morality modified by social traditions. Thus, the condemnation of Alceste in *Le Misanthrope* is not primarily moral, — he is acknowledged to be in a way nearer right than

Célimène who condemns him, — but in the society where he moves he is an anomaly, and he is therefore cast out. Such a judgment is wholly foreign to Jonson's modes of thinking; he would not have understood it, possibly he, too, had not yet "spiritually comprehended the signification of living in society."[1]

Molière is, moreover, more sympathetic and less personal. Jonson scarcely ever emancipates himself from himself, and we feel constantly in his judgments the note of personality. Molière is a spirit apart, personally unaffected by the follies with which he deals, and so able to look upon them with the pure intellect. It is of him that Meredith is thinking in his exquisite description of the comic spirit: "Men's future upon earth does not attract it; their honesty and shapeliness in the present does; and whenever they wax out of proportion, overblown, affected, pretentious, bombastical, hypocritical, pedantic, fantastically delicate; whenever it sees them self-deceived or hoodwinked, given to run riot in idolatries, drifting into vanities, congregating in absurdities, planning shortsightedly, plotting dementedly; whenever they are at variance with their professions, and violate the unwritten but perceptible laws binding them in consideration one to another; whenever they offend sound reason, fair justice; are false in humility or mined with conceit, individually, or in the bulk — the Spirit overhead will

[1] Meredith: *An Essay on Comedy*, p. 69.

look humanely malign and cast an oblique light on them, followed by volleys of silvery laughter. That is the Comic Spirit. . . . To feel its presence and to see it is your assurance that many sane and solid minds are with you in what you are experiencing: and this of itself spares you the pain of satirical heat, and the bitter craving to strike heavy blows. You share the sublime of wrath, that would not have hurt the foolish, but merely demonstrate their foolishness." [1]

The "pain of satirical heat," and the "bitter craving to strike heavy blows," was Jonson's, not Molière's.

Congreve's comedy is yet different. He exposes folly with flashing wit, but he has neither the strenuous morality of Jonson, nor the philosophic aloofness of Molière. His tolerance is that of the experienced man of the world, and his judgments are those of the man of the world.

There is another aspect under which the treatment of character must be considered. To go back once more to the imperfection in character, it has been seen that, if this is to appear comic, the imperfection considered as incongruity must be emphasized. This may be done while the character, as a whole, may still be kept in view — this is Shakespeare's way; or the rest of the character may be relatively disregarded or altogether ignored, and the imperfections on which the comic effect is

[1] *Ib.*, pp. 83–85.

based will thus be made to stand out by themselves. If this goes far enough, the result will be personification of the imperfection, which is now considered as a positive quality — jealousy, vanity, boastfulness, choler, greed. When less pronounced, the result is at least an emphasis on the character considered as a type rather than as an individual. Jonson furnishes in all his plays, except perhaps *The Alchemist* and *Bartholomew Fair*, abundant illustration of this tendency to present the type, while in *The Magnetic Lady* and *The Staple of News* he actually passes over into personification, and the drama lapses, in parts, into allegory. Thus here, again, the author's weaker and less-balanced work shows what is its ultimate tendency.

To the comedy which treats character in this way has been given the name "comedy of humors," from the use of the word "humor" by its representative, Jonson. He has himself well defined his use of the term:

> " As when some one peculiar quality
>   Doth so possess a man that it doth draw
>   All his effects, his spirits, and his powers,
>   In their confluctions, all to run one way,
>   This may be truly said to be a humor," [1]

and these lines are a fair description of the extent to which he selects and isolates characteristics, and exaggerates them somewhat for the purposes of his

---

[1] *Every Man Out of His Humour*, Induction.

treatment. Coleridge's description of Jonson's method is worth placing beside Jonson's own, if we do not allow ourselves to be misled by it:

"Jonson's [characters] are either a man with a huge wen, having a circulation of its own, and which we might conceive amputated, and the patient thereby losing all his character; or they are mere wens themselves instead of men — wens personified, or with eyes, nose, and mouth cut out, mandrake fashion." [1]

Taken as censure, the above is true only of Jonson's inferior work; taken as merely descriptive of a characteristic tendency, it is true of all his work except parts of *Bartholomew Fair* and *The Alchemist*. But it is equally true of Molière, and of Menander, so far as we know him through Terence.

It is rather curious that the extreme tendencies of this kind of comedy should be things so diverse as personal invective and allegory. Their sources, however, are different, the one having its origin in temperamental conditions, the other in intellectual; for the morally judicial temper easily passes over into the personally scornful, while the perception of the faults that produce asymmetry and disproportion in character readily drifts into an excogitation of abstract qualities.

Neither of these tendencies appears to be found in the non-judicial comedy. It is less analytic, and while emphasizing single aspects of individuality it keeps in view the individual. Instead of

[1] Coleridge: *Literary Remains*, Vol. II, p. 279.

the diagrammatic definition of the type, it presents the definiteness of the concrete instance. The contrast between the two methods suggests the difference between the philosophic and the artistic habit, though the parallel cannot be pressed too far.

This is the method of Shakespeare as contrasted with that of Jonson. Molière is somewhere between the two. That he, like Jonson, tends to portray the type is suggested even by the titles of his plays, *The Hypocrite*, *The Miser*, *The Misanthrope;* but his work does not show the extremes that are found in Jonson, "He seized his characters firmly for the central purpose of the play, stamped them in the idea, and by slightly raising and softening the object of study . . . generalized upon it so as to make it permanently human."[1]

It is to be noted that the tendency toward the judicial and the tendency toward the typical are found together predominating in those dramatists in whose plays the comic interests constitute the main plot. This is, it would seem, not a mere coincidence. For there is probably a connection between the judicial attitude and the analytic, type-constructing habit of mind, and there is a connection between these and the kind of mind that constructs such plots. For the kind of mind that sees things in the form of schemes and diagrams, that tends to transform character into char-

---

[1] Meredith : *An Essay on Comedy*, p. 14.

acteristic, will find it natural to construct the sort of plot that suits such treatment. This may be one reason why Jonson invented most of his plots; it may also be a reason why comic authors of his type (Molière, Chapman) often borrowed their comic plots from Plautus and Terence. For these plots, or their Greek model, were originally constructed to fit this sort of comic effect, which may account for the character of the plots, an ingenious complexity, a certain premeditated air and lack of spontaneity, for this is to be referred back to the temper of mind of the author.

On the other hand, the comedy of sympathy is found best in those writers who are also tragic, and often it occurs in the midst of tragedy itself, as in *Lear*. And this, too, is intelligible, if we remember how easily the sympathetic comedy passes into the pathetic and the tragic. Perhaps this is why the sudden transitions from tragedy or pathos to this kind of comedy does not shock us, but, according to its use, either relieves or heightens the tragic effect. Perhaps, too, it was from some such point of view that Plato suggested [1] that the genius of comedy was the same as that of tragedy. Both deal with contrasts, and given the presence of sympathy it is sometimes hard to say where comedy ceases and tragedy begins. It is, moreover, easy to understand why such comedy, being concrete and individual, does not demand a plot made

[1] Plato: *The Symposium*, 324.

especially for it, but more naturally occurs as incidental to any and every plot-action.

In general, an author does not produce both kinds of comedy. There are, however, instances where he wavers between the two; Shakespeare's early comedies seem to show such a wavering, while in Ben Jonson's case it is probable that his romantic comedy, *The Case is Altered*, was in hand at about the same time as *Every Man in His Humour*. Conversely, Shakespeare's Malvolio "sick of self-love" is an instance of reversion to a method of treatment which his mature work had apparently long before abandoned, and the episode of Sir Andrew's duel, also in *Twelfth Night*, was enough in Jonson's style to serve as model for an incident in *The Silent Woman*. Such instances — and they might be multiplied — only go to show that men's minds do not come in fixed moulds or move in fixed grooves. But, in general, it is apparent that the two ways of character-treatment, like the two kinds of plots, and the two attitudes toward character, are the outcome of two different types of mind.

BIBLIOGRAPHIES

———•◦•———

I. LIST OF BOOKS REFERRED TO IN THIS VOLUME

Amiel, H. F.: Journal. London, 1889.

Aristotle: Poetics. Ed. S. H. Butcher. London, 1895.

Brandes, G.: William Shakespeare, A Critical Study. New York, 1898.

Coleridge, S. T.: Literary Remains. Ed. H. N. Coleridge. London, 1836.

Congreve, William: Comedies. Ed. W. E. Henley. Chicago and London, 1895.

Corbin, John: The Elizabethan Hamlet. London and New York, 1895.

Corneille, Pierre: Œuvres. Ed. Mary-Laveaux. Paris, 1862.

Fischer, Rudolf: Zur Kunstentwicklung der Englischen Tragödie von ihren ersten Anfängen bis zu Shakespeare. Strasburg, 1893.

Freytag, Gustav: Die Technik des Dramas. Leipzig, 1894.

Marshall, H. R.: Pain, Pleasure, and Æsthetics. New York, 1894.

Meredith, George: An Essay on Comedy and the Uses of the Comic Spirit. New York, 1897.

Paget, Violet (Vernon Lee): Studies of the Eighteenth Century in Italy. London, 1887.

Plato: The Dialogues. Trans. B. Jowett. New York and London, 1892.

Sidney, Sir Philip: Defense of Poesy. Ed. Albert S. Cook. Boston, 1890.

Shelley, P. B.: The Cenci.

Sophocles: The Plays and Fragments, with critical notes, commentary, and translation in English prose. R. C. Jebb. Cambridge, 1894.

Ulrici, H.: Shakespeare's Dramatic Art. Trans. L. D. Schmitz. London, 1876.

Wendell, Barrett: William Shakespeare.

Woodbridge, E.: Studies in Jonson's Comedy. Boston, 1898.

II. LIST OF TREATISES DEALING WITH DRAMATIC THEORY AND CRITICISM [1]

Archer, William: About the Theatre. Essays and Studies. London, 1886.

——, English Dramatists of To-day. London, 1882.

Everett, C. C.: Poetry, Comedy, and Duty. New York, 1890.

Fitzgerald, Percy: Principles of Comedy and Dramatic Effect. London, 1870.

Freytag, Gustav: The Technique of the Drama. Trans. E. J. MacEwan. Chicago, 1895.

Hazlitt, William: English Comic Writers. Lecture VIII.

Hennequin, Alfred: The Art of Playwriting. Boston, 1891.

Hugo, Victor: Prefaces to *Cromwell* and *Hernani* (written 1827, 1830).

Hunt, Leigh: Dramatic Essays. Ed. William Archer and R. W. Lowe. London, 1896.

Irving, Henry: The Drama. New York, 1892.

Jones, Henry Arthur: The Renascence of the English Drama. London, 1895.

[1] For references on English drama, cf. the excellent bibliography by K. L. Bates and L. B. Godfrey, Wellesley College, 1896.

Lamb, Charles: Dramatic Essays. Ed. Brander Matthews. New York, 1891.

Morris, Mowbray : Essays in Theatrical Criticism. London, 1882.

Meredith, George: An Essay on Comedy, and the Uses of the Comic Spirit. New York, 1897.

Moulton, R. G.: Shakespeare as a Dramatic Artist. Oxford, 1889.

Polti, Georges: Les Trente-six Situations Dramatiques. Paris, 1895.

Prölss, R.: Katechismus der Dramaturgie. Leipzig, 1877.

Shaw, G. B.: Articles on the drama in the *Saturday Review* up to 1898.

Souriau, Maurice: De la Convention dans la Tragédie Classique et dans le Drame Romantique. Paris, 1885.

Thoma, A.: Das Drama. Gotha, 1891.

Wagner, Wilhelm Richard: Oper und Drama. Leipzig, 1852.

Walkley, A. B.: Playhouse Impressions. London, 1892.

III. LIST OF WORKS THAT WILL BE OF VALUE IN THE STUDY OF CLASSICAL DRAMA [1]

Butcher, S. H.: Aristotle's Theory of Poetry and Fine Art, with a critical text and a translation of the Poetics. London and New York, 1895; 2d ed., 1898.

——, Some Aspects of the Greek Genius.

Campbell, Lewis: A Guide to Greek Tragedy for English Readers. New York and London, 1891.

Collins, J. Churton: Menander. In Essays and Studies. London, 1895.

[1] With two exceptions, this list does not include translations of the classical authors. Jebb's edition of Sophocles is mentioned because of its invaluable introductions and notes, and the surpassing excellence of its translation ; the translations of Seneca — the first in English since those by Lodge — are noted because they are new and as yet little known.

Fischer, Rudolf: Zur Kunstentwicklung der Englischen Tragödie von ihren ersten Anfängen bis zu Shakespeare. Strasburg, 1893.

Freytag, Gustav: Technique of the Drama. Trans. E. J. MacEwan. Chicago, 1895.

Haigh, A. E.: The Attic Theatre. Oxford, 1889.

——, The Tragic Drama of the Greeks. Oxford, 1896.

Jebb, R. C.: The Growth and Influence of Classical Greek Poetry. Boston and New York, 1893.

——, Introductions, etc., accompanying translation of Sophocles.

Moulton, R. G.: The Ancient Classical Drama: A Study in Literary Evolution. Oxford, 1890.

Seneca: *Medea*, and *The Daughters of Troy*. Metrical translation, Ella I. Harris. Boston, 1898.

Sophocles: The Plays and Fragments. Prose translation, R. C. Jebb. Cambridge, 1883-96.

Verrall, A. W.: The Student's Manual of Greek Tragedy. London and New York, 1891.

INDEX

———◆———

179